EPIDEMIOLOGY AND MENTAL ILLNESS

Joint Commission
on Mental Illness and Health

MONOGRAPH SERIES / NO. 6

Epidemiology and Mental Illness

RICHARD J. PLUNKETT
JOHN E. GORDON

A REPORT TO THE STAFF DIRECTOR, JACK R. EWALT
1960

Basic Books, Inc., Publishers, New York

Foreword

T HIS IS the sixth of a series of monographs to be published by
the Joint Commission on Mental Illness and Health as part
of a national mental health survey that will culminate in a
final report containing findings and recommendations for a
national mental health program.

The present document constitutes a report of the project
director to the staff director of the Joint Commission.

Titles of the monograph series, together with the principal
authors, are listed here in the order of expected publication:

1. *Current Concepts of Positive Mental Health*
   Marie Jahoda, Ph.D., Basic Books, 1958. $2.75.

2. *Economics of Mental Illness*
   Rashi Fein, Ph.D., Basic Books, 1958. $3.00.

3. *Mental Health Manpower Trends*
   George W. Albee, Ph.D., Basic Books, 1959. $6.75.

4. *Americans View Their Mental Health*. A Nationwide Inter-
   view Survey
   Gerald Gurin, Ph.D., Joseph Veroff, Ph.D., and Sheila
   Feld, Ph.D.

5. *Community Resources in Mental Health*
   Reginald Robinson, Ph.D., David F. DeMarche, Ph.D., and
   Mildred K. Wagle, M.S.S.A.

These monographs, each a part of an over-all study design, will contain the detailed information forming the basis of a final report. From the data in the individual studies and other relevant information, the headquarters staff will prepare a summary document incorporating its findings and recommendations for national and state mental health programs. This summary document will have the approval of the Joint Commission before its publication in the form of an official report.

This final report will be published by Basic Books and transmitted to the United States Congress, the Surgeon General of the Public Health Services, and the Governors of the States, together with their representatives in the public health and mental health professions, in accordance with the provisions of the Mental Health Study Act of 1955.

Participating organizations, members and officers of the Joint Commission and the headquarters staff are listed in an appendix at the end of the book.

The Joint Commission, it may be seen, is a nongovernmental, multidisciplinary, nonprofit organization representing a variety of national agencies concerned with mental health. Its study was authorized by a unanimous resolution of Congress and is financed by grants from the following sources:

American Association on Mental Deficiency
American Association of Psychiatric Clinics for Children
American Legion
American Medical Association
American Occupational Therapy Association
American Orthopsychiatric Association, Inc.
American Psychiatric Association
American Psychoanalytic Association
Association for Physical and Mental Rehabilitation
Carter Products Company
Catholic Hospital Association
Field Foundation
Henry Hornblower Fund
National Association for Mental Health
National Committee Against Mental Illness
National Institute of Mental Health
National League for Nursing
National Rehabilitation Association
Rockefeller Brothers Fund
Benjamin Rosenthal Foundation
Smith, Kline and French Foundation

Additional copies of *Epidemiology and Mental Illness* may be purchased from the publisher or from book dealers.

JOINT COMMISSION ON MENTAL ILLNESS AND HEALTH

Staff Review

T HE RELEVANCE of epidemiology to mental illness may seem questionable at first glance, especially if one is accustomed to associating this discipline with the control of infectious diseases. The fact is that epidemiology, as the science that studies the factors initiating and controlling the appearance of disease in populations, may be destined to provide much of the information and guidance on which public health authorities of the future will base their approach to the problem of mental illness. Anyone who doubts the existence of an "epidemic" of mental illness in the United States should ponder on the estimate that there may be as many as 17,500,000 Americans who have psychiatric disorders severe enough to warrant treatment.

What kind of contribution can we expect of the epidemiologist? First, we can ask him to count the number of mentally ill in the population at a given time and to measure the rate at which new cases appear. If he has accurate methods of diagnosis, he may also measure the morbidity of various disease entities and assess their relative importance.

Second, we can expect the epidemiologist to uncover and evaluate many of the factors that are, or appear to be, associated with mental illness in a population. There are such countless variables as age, sex, marital status, presence of physical disease, and socio-economic position; some may be associated with mental illness in an individual or group under certain conditions and not under others, and combinations without end are possible.

Third, we can hope that the epidemiologist—as he observes the complex interplay of factors in ecology—will identify patterns of association between mental illness and factors affecting the individual and the group, patterns suggestive of a causal relationship.

Finally, after he has accumulated sufficient meaningful data, we can look to the epidemiologist for guidance in the conception of public health programs for the prevention and control of mental illness.

What progress has epidemiology made in these respects, and what can reasonably be expected of it in the mental health field in the future? These, essentially, are the questions that motivated the study headed by Richard J. Plunkett, Associate Director of the Joint Commission and Secretary of the Council on Mental Health of the American Medical Association. The study was fortunate to have as its consultant John E. Gordon, Professor Emeritus of Epidemiology at the Harvard School of Public Health and a pioneer in the extension of his specialty to such widely divergent problems as highway accidents and overpopulation.

After tracing the historical origins of an epidemiology of mental illness, the authors demonstrate its relevance against the background of medical ecology—the interrelation of man and his environment. There follows an analysis of the rather significant limitations of current clinical knowledge which, to an important degree, must be the point of departure for fruitful application of epidemiology to the investigation of mass disease. These limitations are of particular moment because they reveal some of the basic shortcomings that hamper progress in the clinical understanding and treatment of mental illness. One of them is the inability of psychiatry to evolve accepted classifications of mental disease entities that can be applied with confidence to problems of diagnosis. A more fundamental limitation is the disheartening dearth of information about the causes of mental illness; this is a serious gap in the body of basic knowledge, and it is responsible for many of our clinical difficulties.

The authors stress the fact that the etiology of mental illness is multifactorial and bring into their discussion some interesting evidence to suggest that mental turmoil or emotional stress is communicable under certain circumstances.

The sources of epidemiologic data are examined and also found wanting. Hospital data have been of limited value because of variations in the standards, policies, and availability of facilities and because they exclude the great majority of mentally ill who escape institutionalization by virtue of the relative mildness of their symptoms. Special attention is given several community surveys of mental illness; the critique of their orientation, methodology, and findings is a sound evaluation of this epidemiologic technique and its shortcomings.

Drs. Plunkett and Gordon believe that epidemiology must now construct "orderly, well-controlled field experiments designed to identify and quantitate, one by one, the various factors that have been advanced as being involved in causality." They set forth a general plan for such a pilot study and suggest that suicide, alcoholism, postpartum psychoses, and psychosomatic illnesses are well adapted to the method they propose.

The authors approach their subject with caution. In their estimation, the value of the epidemiologic approach to mental illness is largely potential, dependent as it is upon the existence of a body of scientific knowledge only now in the early stages of assembly. In the meantime, the epidemiologist should concentrate on etiology, tracing lines of causality from observations of factors in the mass that are not apparent from an examination of the individual.

Epidemiology reminds us that no man is sufficient unto himself, that mental illness—perhaps more so than any other scourge of humanity—is a by-product of man's social existence in a complex environment of his own making. Much, of course, can be gained by studying the pathological process in the individual; but complete understanding can be approached only as mental illness is viewed in the light of man's eternal striving to adapt himself to the demands of his destiny.

JACK R. EWALT, M.D., *Director*

Acknowledgments

As A MEANS of orienting ourselves in the multifactorial, non-specific etiology of functional mental illness, we obtained the viewpoints of a number of scientists and scholars, the majority of whom took part in a symposium on the etiology of mental illness at the National Health Forum of the National Health Council in Cincinnati in 1957. The following persons generously contributed working papers which formed an essential background to an epidemiologic viewpoint and approach, and we are indebted to them:

Reverend George C. Anderson, Director, Academy of Religion and Mental Health.

R. W. Gerard, M.D., Mental Health Research Institute, University of Michigan.

Harriet L. Hardy, M.D., Assistant Medical Director in charge of Occupational Medical Service, Department of Medicine, Massachusetts Institute of Technology.

Jules Henry, Ph.D., Professor of Anthropology, Washington University.

Franz J. Kallmann, M.D., Professor of Psychiatry, Columbia University, College of Physicians and Surgeons.

M. Ralph Kaufman, M.D., Director, Psychiatric Services, Mount Sinai Hospital, New York City.

Charles Morris, Ph.D., Lecturer in Philosophy, University of Chicago.

Norman Polansky, Ph.D., Associate Professor, School of Social Science, Western Reserve University.

Nevitt Sanford, Ph.D., Professor of Psychology, Department of Psychology, University of California.

Franklin Top, M.D., Professor and Head, Department of Hygiene and Preventive Medicine, State University of Iowa, College of Medicine.

We wish to make special acknowledgment to Leo Srole, coauthor of *Midtown Manhattan: The Mental Health Story,* and to Alexander Leighton, who assumed direction of the Midtown survey after the death of its senior author, Thomas A. C. Rennie, for giving us access to their manuscript prior to its publication.

We wish also to make special acknowledgment to Ray E. Trussell and Jack Elinson for giving us access to data from their Hunterdon County, New Jersey, study prior to its publication.

We are indebted to Mrs. Charnya Fisher, Ambellur N. D. Frederick, and Miss Helene DeMillar for their valuable services as research assistants, and to Miss Mary Elizabeth Hoare, secretary of the project.

RICHARD J. PLUNKETT, M.D.
JOHN E. GORDON, M.D.

Contents

EPIDEMIOLOGY AND MENTAL ILLNESS

I

Introduction

THE OBJECTIVES of medicine and public health are the prevention and control of illness. Scientific knowledge basic to these pursuits is acquired by three methods equally fundamental to an understanding of mental or physical disease. They are clinical observation, laboratory experiment, and epidemiologic analysis.

Clinical observation is the oldest, the most empirical, and the most direct, for it begins at the bedside of the sick individual. The controlled conditions of laboratory experimentation are the principal reliance of modern medical science. Both of these approaches are primarily directed at disease in the individual.

The epidemiologic method, on the other hand, is concerned with the field observation of disease under natural conditions in whole populations. Here the patient is a group of persons, sometimes many thousands, including both the sick and the well. The frequency with which different diseases occur in different fractions of the population is studied in terms of time and place. These segments of groups range from such relatively simple divisions as those of age, race, and sex to occupation and social and economic status.

None of the three approaches by itself can lead to a full understanding of the prevention and control of illness. Emphasis shifts from one to another as knowledge advances, and a combination of effort often hastens results. Furthermore, modern field practice in epidemiology tends increasingly to include all three elements. No analysis is better than the basic data from which it is derived, and these issue primarily from clinical study of the individual. A field laboratory has long been essential to the investigation of disease in nature, first for the communicable diseases and progressively for the chronic noninfectious conditions that are equally occupying the attention of the epidemiologist.

The peculiar characteristic of epidemiology, then, is not so much the method as the unit of observation, the population. A specific population, through the interaction of its members, has physical and mental characteristics as capable of being defined as those of the individual. The singular contribution of epidemiology is toward a more sophisticated understanding of the group determinants of disease in the mass—the factors affecting its manifestations in the population. Effective steps for the prevention and control of disease—mental and physical—are not possible unless knowledge about the individual is extended to encompass the group.

Neither the clinical, the experimental, nor the epidemiologic approach to mental illness has to date borne much fruit in these respects. Disorders of the mind have eluded the kind of clinical and experimental measurement that has been so successfully applied to those of the body. Many forms of mental illness, especially those of apparently functional origin, have for centuries defied attempts at scientific classification into definitive and universally recognized clinical entities. When observers are unable to agree on what they are looking at, they are likely not to have a clear conception of its origin. In the absence of a common descriptive language, efforts to discover the etiology of all but a few organic mental diseases have met with ill success. Consequently, progress in the prevention and control of mental illness in populations has been so slow as to be almost nonexistent.

It is our purpose to discuss the limitations of current scientific knowledge about mental disease and to show how they have distorted the results of various attempts to study its effects in populations. At first glance, these limitations seem to imply that the time is not yet ripe for the serious application of epidemiologic methods to the field. Closer study, however, suggests that the relatively new application of this old discipline may itself be able to contribute much of the knowledge on which to base programs for prevention and control, those matters being its direct concern.

Mental illness is a problem of massive proportions. It has been estimated that 17,500,000 Americans are suffering from mental illness severe enough to warrant treatment. Slightly more than 10 per cent of these, approximately 1,814,000, are recognizable during the course of a year; this is the number treated in hospitals, clinics, or by private psychiatrists. Nearly 90 per cent of mental illness escapes recognition and, consequently, any possibility of treatment, control, or prevention.

It is the task of epidemiology to define the size and content of this vast problem. Clinical and experimental weapons have only made a dent on that small segment of the problem which annually comes to the attention of the treatment facilities of society; yet, it is unthinkable that the scientist should refrain from directing a coordinated attack on mass mental illness until knowledge of its origin and course in the individual is on a par with that of the communicable diseases.

In this volume we hope to suggest a beginning.

II

The Epidemiologic Method: A New Approach to an Old Problem

A SYSTEMATIC EPIDEMIOLOGIC approach is relatively new to the study of mental illness and, indeed, to many areas outside the field of acute communicable diseases where it was first applied. Understandably, it is viewed in varying perspective by psychiatrists, physicians, social scientists, and other workers who have long been laboring with these difficult and complex disorders.

Epidemiology is regarded by some as a mathematical adding up of cases in an attempt to bring depth and proportion to a problem of unknown dimensions; others dismiss it with good-natured banter about "not knowing insanity was contagious." Occasionally its unfamiliar methods are embraced indiscriminately in the hope that they will somehow introduce order into a labyrinth of causation and course. Although none of these views is correct, epidemiology has yet to find its appropriate place among the various disciplines in the mental health field.

ORIGIN OF AN EPIDEMIOLOGY
OF MENTAL ILLNESS

The chronic nature of most mental disorders accounts in large measure for the delayed application of the epidemiologic method to their study. For years this discipline concentrated almost exclusively on acute diseases, mainly infection in masses of cases—epidemics that were common, sometimes overwhelming, and occasionally world-wide.

The acute situations in psychiatry, on the other hand, are usually exacerbations of chronic processes in the individual. Killing epidemics such as cholera and plague, even typhoid fever and dysentery, have no counterparts in psychiatry.

Epidemiologists eventually recognized that they had to investigate the endemic behavior of disease if they were to understand the rise and fall of epidemics. Tuberculosis and syphilis, for example, are essentially endemic, yet they rank high among causes of morbidity and mortality. This new emphasis first centered on the infections and then was broadened to include traumatic injuries, particularly those associated with accidents, that are equally as acute in origin as infections but are more sporadic and endemic in their distribution.

As one communicable disease after another came under control, public health enlarged its activities to include the chronic and mainly noninfectious processes that were increasingly becoming major causes of death. This trend in public health gave rise to an epidemiology of chronic disease. Mental illness is one of the most widespread chronic diseases—and the least measurable—in the population.

For many years, statistical data on mental disorders had been collected principally in relation to hospital patients and primarily for administrative purposes. Some order began to emerge when, in 1903, the Bellevue Hospital in New York proposed its classification of mental diseases. Although he gives the original credit to Milton J. Rosenau, Henry B. Elkind (1927, 1938) was among the first to suggest that these data could be used for epidemiologic purposes. At the First International Congress on Mental Hygiene, Haven Emerson (1932) offered quantitative evidence of the magnitude of the problem; some years later Emerson (1938) outlined an epidemiologic approach. Allen Freeman (1939), who was first in so many fields of epidemiology, inspired a comprehensive field survey of mental illness in Baltimore.

As mental illness was progressively incorporated into modern public health activities, and trained public health workers were attracted to the field, epidemiologic studies served as natural precursors to formal programs for prevention and control. New York and Massachusetts took the lead among the official state agencies, and the United States Public Health Service was active nationally.

The psychiatric problems of the Armed Forces during World War II further stimulated the group approach to mental disorders. Preventive psychiatry was developed through an epidemiologic approach to such an extent that the association of mental health and epidemiology came to be accepted procedure in operational activities in the field, in the management of recruits, and at administrative levels.

This emphasis gained ground in the postwar years. The annual conferences of the Milbank Memorial Fund did much to crystallize thought in this area. Increasing attention is currently being given to technical methods, and long-term studies are under way in several centers in the United States and Canada.

Much of the responsibility for his delayed interest in the mass behavior of mental illness rests with the epidemiologist himself. When he finally saw the need to incorporate chronic disease within the scope of his interests and sought methods and techniques applicable to the study of these conditions, the professional worker in the mental illness field recognized his own obligation and grasped the opportunity to include these new viewpoints in his practice and research.

EPIDEMIOLOGY AS MEDICAL ECOLOGY

The most satisfactory insight into the methods and objectives of epidemiology can be achieved by viewing it essentially as an organized approach to human ecology, specifically medical ecology, by way of scientific observation and analysis. Ecology deals with the mutual relations between man and his environment, seeing disease and health as selected instances among the possible results of this total interaction (John E. Gordon, 1958a).

The health of the individual or of the species is the achievement of a dominance of positive adaptations to environment. Disease is the dominance of negative or unfavorable adaptations, a poor result of the dynamics of ecology, the extent and severity of which depend on the nature of the biological and social equilibrium between human host and environment. Thus, the relative ascendancy of health or disease is a dynamic state, and the unfavorable adaptations as they occur are assessed in terms of the clinical nature, locale, and duration of the ensuing disease and the number of persons affected.

The heritage of modern man carries along a substantial substratum of mental illness. The human central nervous system evolved under the simple conditions of a community life close to nature. As the environment grew more complex, positive adaptations became more difficult. To whatever degree it has been successful, this process has left residual strains, especially evident in certain personality types.

The appearance and accumulation of these stresses suggest that ecology is well suited to the analysis of mental disorders. Its main contribution can be a unifying influence, a marshaling of the biological and social sciences for an organized attack on the reasons for man's failure to adapt.

THE FUNCTIONS OF EPIDEMIOLOGY

Epidemiology is a body of knowledge about the occurrence and behavior of disease in populations and, also, a method of study to determine causes and courses of diseases affecting the individual and the community. As an applied science, it is an important diagnostic and research discipline of public health.

Careful examination is as necessary a prelude to effective treatment when the patient is a population as it is when he is an individual. A diagnosis is just as essential in either case. In fact, the two merge in modern medical practice where management of the individual and his illness is incomplete except in the context of family and environment.

A practical objective of epidemiologic research is to supply the facts on which to base improved clinical practice and community management. The first requisite is to define the limits of the problem, the extent to which mental disorders affect the population. The second is to separate component diseases and abnormalities, evaluating each individually and in relation to the others. Their relative significance is weighed in terms of the death, permanent defects, and duration of temporary disability that they produce. These steps direct investigation toward the means for control. Our initial task, then, is to determine the broad nature and extent of the problem.

Prevalence: The Status Quo

The prevalence of mental illness in a community is determined by the ratio of the recognized cases present at a designated time to the total population. The procedure is theoretically simple, but administratively difficult. Since mental diseases are not reportable by law, investigators have been forced to rely historically on indirect sources of information which, in most instances, were not intended for statistical purposes. This approach is highly inexact because of limitations in knowledge, deficiencies in nomenclature and classification, and lack of satisfactory case-finding techniques. In short, the problem has been and still is: what do we count, how do we define it, and how do we measure it?

Arbitrary or operational definitions of mental illness have, of course, been adopted. This course has inherent drawbacks: a workable definition almost invariably eliminates characteristics that should be included; a specific characteristic may be so restricted by definition that measurement is all but purposeless; and the results are liable to apply not universally but only to the population selected.

Deaths provide a ready index of many medical conditions because they are a matter of official record by law. A satisfactory knowledge of case fatality may give a working approximation of incidence; with additional facts about the average duration of illness, a fair idea of prevalence can be achieved. Although mental disorders account for many illnesses, they result directly in but few deaths, except for suicide. As an index of the frequency of mental illness generally, therefore, deaths are of no value.

Information on the occurrence of mental disorders must be sought elsewhere, either from existing data commonly collected for other purposes or through direct population surveys.

Institutional data perforce are drawn from an ill-defined population and are colored by changing fashions in nomenclature, the availability of facilities, and policies governing admissions. The ends of epidemiology require that frequency of mental disease be determined according to clinical entities or etiologic criteria. The general prevalence of mental illness is more accurately assessed when it is projected on the basis of accumulated frequencies of disease entities arrived at by precise criteria rather than on the basis of approximate qualitative terms.

At any rate, workers seeking to grasp the prevalence of mental illness have relied principally on direct survey methods, expensive as they are in time and money, restricted in their application, and susceptible to the pitfalls of population-sampling, case-finding, identification, and classification of illness.

Incidence: The Trend

Periodic determinations of prevalence offer a clue to the dynamic, shifting nature of mass disease. A more reliable measure of these changes, however, depends on rates of incidence, the number of new cases cropping up in the population within prescribed limits of time, usually one year. Inferences derived from these observations are leads in the search for cause.

✓ Prevalence and incidence rates combine to indicate the absolute size of the problem, its relative size in comparison with other known classes of mass disease, and whether it is increasing or decreasing. The two indices are compiled from the same sources of data, with rare exceptions.

Causality in Mass Disease

Factors in the causality of mass disease fall into two broad divisions, those related to characteristics of the host, and those residing in the environment, of which the specific agent of disease is one among several (Gordon *et al.*, 1952). The concept of multifactorial causation does not discount the specificity of known agents; rather, it recognizes the specific—indispensable as it may be—as no more than one among several contributing factors.

The older view of etiology assumed a fixed mosaic of causality, with different elements in ordered relation to each other. In time, the search for a simplified concept led to emphasis on the most tangible and direct feature, the specific agent. The gain was more precise knowledge about one component of causality, but the loss was a de-emphasis on the multifactorial nature of etiology and neglect of the important fact that the inciting agent is not necessarily the only factor in the disease process.

When disease is viewed in the mass, something more is required of a concept of causality than the discovery of the means by which the process comes into being. Factors determining its course must also be recognized. When a disease attacks a population, it sometimes erupts as an isolated case; more rarely, and at the other extreme, it causes an epidemic. Yet both events may be temporary, the disease subsiding or disappearing for long periods, or perhaps permanently in a particular region. Or it may become firmly entrenched, but again variably, occasionally at an endemic level, more commonly with irregular or periodic fluctuations in incidence that may even surge to epidemic proportions.

The origin of mass disease processes and the subsequent pattern of their epidemiologic behavior are so fundamentally determined by the initial ecologic situation as to be inseparable. Knowledge of the principles governing disease as a mass phenomenon, and the techniques for its study, arose from observations of infections—superb ecologic examples of one organism reacting with another in a common environment. As the epidemiologic method was extended to other mass diseases, and even to injuries, the same general means for interpretation of cause and course were found to apply.

Mass illness is the domination, in varying degrees, of disease-producing forces over those providing protection. The result is a departure from the equilibrium of health. The direction of effect and the extent of reaction are laid down by the victorious components of a complex and variable causal system. This postulate is pertinent to an understanding of the etiology of mental illness.

A practical approach to the investigation of cause should proceed from analysis to synthesis. Single causal factors must first be identified and evaluated in the light of their independent effect by measuring incidence and recording the character of the movement of a disorder through the population. The second step is to trace the interaction of multiple factors by means of multivariable statistical procedures.

The Strategy of Control

The first obligation of the epidemiologist, then, in collaboration with the clinician and laboratory scientist, is to identify disease as a biological process and as it affects individuals in a population. Having determined that the disease in the individual represents a significant deviation from the accepted physiologic norm, the epidemiologist projects this knowledge to the study of the population, defining the mass problem, the forces that created it and their probable influence on its future course, the proportions of people affected, the time relationships, and the geographical distribution and frequency of the disease.

It is then the responsibility of the public health administrator to put this information to practical use.

The attack is directed toward the dominant factors of cause and course. Strategy considers the relative importance to be assigned various measures of control: some of the causative factors are biological, others sociological; some relate to the host, others to the environment; a specific agent may or may not be implicated. Realistic appraisal must be made of control measures vis-à-vis community resources, public reaction, and other crucial aspects of the total situation. From these considerations emerges a practical plan for control, hammered out by the combined efforts of administrator, epidemiologist, and clinician.

Existing knowledge suffices for control of most infections. Knowledge of heart disease and cancer is less sure. It is so inadequate in the field of mental disease that practical control programs are no more than conjectural.

Although implementation of the control program is the administrator's job in his capacity as the agent of society, it is left to the epidemiologist to evaluate results and to supply the executive with data for judging the validity of his methods. This is an invariable requirement of any program, especially if it entails new modes of control and prevention, for it may have been constructed on a false premise, sound measures may have been poorly executed, or the causative factors may have changed since the initial observations on which the program was based.

III

The Doctor's Dilemma: Definitions and Diagnoses

METHOD IS no less essential to the study of mass disease than it is to clinical and laboratory investigation. A certain amount of empiricism is unavoidable, but solid achievement rests on the logical, progressive construction of a body of tested knowledge within the framework of a universal method.

The epidemiologic method begins by identifying and evaluating qualitatively the general class of disease under study. Then it is analyzed in detail and its components classified in an orderly grouping of entities according to their related intrinsic and extrinsic characteristics. When the problem has been defined in universally acceptable terms, the search for cause and course can get under way. Then the concept of prevalence takes on meaning, because quantitative progress presupposes a degree of qualitative success.

Epidemiology has contributed to an understanding of mass

physical diseases because most of them were nailed down long ago as clinical entities. The salient diagnostic features of plague, typhoid fever, diphtheria, malaria, measles, and other infectious diseases have been universally recognized for many years, in some cases since ancient times. Crude methods of treatment, control, and prevention were successful long before etiology, as in cholera, was clearly understood. Thus the modern science of epidemiology inherited a ready-made language and the elements of a method that it was able to adapt effectively to its own purposes as new problems of non-communicable diseases came to the fore.

Disorders of the mind, with relatively few exceptions, have persistently resisted pigeonholing in spite of countless attempts to put them in their place. A few of the frankly organic illnesses such as general paresis are readily identified. But schizophrenia, the most widespread of all mental diseases (if indeed it is an entity), is only beginning to succumb to the diagnostic attack, and the same can be said of other diseases considered to be more psychogenic than organic, whose symptoms are as tangled as their etiology.

IS THERE METHOD TO MADNESS?

A passage from the 1843 Annual Report of the McLean Asylum, a private mental institution in Waverley, Massachusetts, is remarkably relevant today (Luther V. Bell, 1844, pp. 28–29):

No reason has presented itself to justify receding from the views presented for several years past, of the unsoundness and consequent uselessness of what are called the *statistics* of insanity. Every year's experience convinces me that those facts regarding this subject, which are capable of being arithmetically noted, are of too little moment to be worth recording at all, while those circumstances touching the duration, form, symptoms and event of cases, which would be truly important are, from their nature, incapable of being generalized tabularly into even a loose approximation to the truth. Statistics are doubtless valuable in relation to topics where accuracy is capable of being approached, but not in a legitimate mode of expressing mere opinions.

I still find it impracticable in a vast proportion of cases, to fix with any certainty the point at which the mind lost its balance, and by which the duration of disease before admission can be determined, notwithstanding the great body of our inmates are from the intelligent and educated classes of society, where facts of this sort are attainable, if at all. I still find insanity rarely produced from a single cause, so marked as to permit being tabularized accurately, but by a combination or accidental coincidence of causes, moral, physical and educational.

The almost whimsical naïveté with which nosologists of one hundred years ago viewed the causes of mental illness is illustrated in a table of moral and physical causes of insanity (Richard J. Dunglison, 1860, p. 656).

After surveying 11,259 cases, the article listed among the "moral" causes: domestic troubles; mental anxiety; religious anxiety; financial difficulties, reversals of fortune, etc.; excessive study or application to business; loss of friends; disappointment in love, ambition, etc.; fear and fright; defective education; uncontrollable temper; nostalgia; political excitement.

"Physical" causes were defined as: ill health and unclassified diseases; fever; epilepsy; cerebral disease; paralysis; intemperance and dissipation; conditions peculiar to women; vicious habits and indulgences; wounds and blows; excessive use of opium, tobacco, etc.; exposure and loss of sleep; over-exertion; old age; spiritualism; exposure to sun and heat.

Isaac Ray (1871, p. 310) expressed the bewilderment of the diagnostician:

Then here is monomania and melancholia. How are they to be distinguished from each other? The two terms were once applied to the same form of disease, and I doubt if there is much agreement yet as to the exact meaning of monomania. No man can be sure when he speaks of a certain form of insanity that he means by it precisely what everybody else does. There might be a difference of opinion as to the exact form to which a certain case should be referred, and that would make the statistics utterly useless.

One of the first attempts at organized classification was *A Nomenclature of Diseases and Conditions and Rules for the Recording and Filing of Histories for Bellevue and Allied Hospitals* (Bellevue Hospital, 1903). It included a section on diseases of the nervous system and was widely adopted by the large eastern general hospitals and, to some extent, by state mental hospitals. The list was revised in 1911 and again in 1922 to conform to international efforts at classification; the latter edition embodied a system of numerical coding.

Meanwhile, the National Committee for Mental Hygiene met with the American Medico-Psychological Association (forerunner of the American Psychiatric Association) and published the *Statistical Manual for the Use of Institutions for the Insane* (National Committee For Mental Hygiene, 1918). Twenty-two clinical groups, most of them psychoses, were listed, and each diagnosis was accompanied by a short explanation of how and where it should be employed. The *Manual,* revised in 1923, was adopted by a number of state mental institutions.

Under the editorship of H. Burton Logie (1933), a *Standard Classified Nomenclature of Disease* was published as the outcome of a national conference on nomenclature attended by representatives of all the major medical and specialty groups. Unfortunately, the American Psychiatric Association and the American Neurological Association were unable to compromise their diagnostic differences, and it was necessary to list separately the generally duplicating classifications of each under "Disease of the Psychobiologic Unit." To further complicate matters, similar or identical diagnoses accepted by both groups were coded differently by each.

Four years later this work was revised under the auspices of the American Medical Association, and it was again revised and renamed *The Standard Nomenclature of Disease and Standard Nomenclature of Operations* (Edwin Jordan, 1942).

The deluge of psychiatric disorders uncovered or touched off by World War II led the Armed Forces and the Veterans Administration to make extensive revisions in nomenclature that threw the entire field into confusion. Four years before the 1952 revision of the *Standard Nomenclature* was due, the Committee on Nomenclature and Statistics of the American Psychiatric Association surveyed the chaos and prepared for reform. The result was the *Diagnostic and Statistical Manual* (American Psychiatric Association, 1952, pp. vii–viii) which commented in retrospect:

By 1948, then, the situation in psychiatric nomenclature had deteriorated almost to the point of confusion which existed throughout medical nomenclature in the twenties. At least three nomenclatures (Standard, Armed Forces, and Veterans Administration) were in general use, and none of them fell accurately into line with the International Statistical Classification. One agency found itself in the uncomfortable position of using one nomenclature for clinical use, a different one for disability rating, and the International for statistical work. In addition, practically every teaching center had made modifications of the Standard for its own use and assorted modifications of the Armed Forces nomenclature had been introduced into many clinics and hospitals by psychiatrists returning from military duty.

Following the adoption of new nomenclatures by the Army and Veterans Administration, the Committee on Nomenclature and Statistics of the American Psychiatric Association postponed change in its recommended official nomenclature pending some evidence as to the usability of the new systems. In 1948, the Committee undertook to learn from the Army and the Veterans Administration how successful the changes had been, and what the shortcomings of the new systems were. Simultaneously, an effort was made to determine the sentiments of the membership regarding the need for a change in the then current Standard.

A high percentage of psychiatrists contacted felt that change in the nomenclature was urgently needed, with special attention to the areas of personality disorders and transient reactions to special stress. The need for change seemed to be felt more strongly by those in clinic and private practice than by those in mental hospital or institutional work. However, a considerable proportion of mental hospital staffs urged change; this was especially true where outpatient clinics had been established in connection with the hospitals.

The Army and Veterans Administration reported that their revisions were considered successful by clinicians and statisticians. Statistically, the revisions were said to be more easily handled than the old nomenclatures, particularly when it became necessary to code diagnoses into the revised International. After some expected initial difficulties in using the new terms, clinicians reported that the revisions were more useful than the old listing. Psychiatrists who had become accustomed to the revised nomenclature in the Army were unwilling to return to the Standard Nomenclature upon return to civilian life. The major shortcoming in both revisions was reported to be the classification of mental disorders accompanying organic brain disease, a minor problem in military psychiatry but a major item in civilian psychiatry.

The American Psychiatric Association's classification was incorporated in the *Standard Nomenclature of Diseases and Operations* (Richard J. Plunkett, 1952), and the terminology and coding of the American Psychiatric Association and the American Medical Association were at last identical.

The *Standard Nomenclature* is accepted and in use in 75 to 85 per cent of all general hospitals in the United States; the American Psychiatric Association's companion *Diagnostic and Statistical Manual* has been adopted by virtually all of the state mental institutions. In spite of continuing diagnostic differences among physicians and hospitals, the general acceptance of descriptive terminology and classification represents for the epidemiologist a heartening beginning in the long-range accumulation of meaningful data.

Unfortunately, international nomenclature has been following somewhat divergent lines since 1948. The *Manual of the International Statistical Classification of Diseases, Injuries and Causes of Death* (World Health Organization, 1948), revised in 1955, was the culmination of a long struggle to effect an international compromise in diagnostic classification. Although its usefulness in establishing a supranational language cannot be minimized, it moves toward the very diffuseness in psychiatric classification that the American Medical Association and the American Psychiatric Association have striven to clarify. The proponents of the *International Classification* are pushing with some success for its adoption by American hospitals. It is to be hoped that general hospitals with psychiatric services and mental institutions in the United States will adhere to the 1952 nomenclature and that efforts directed to the universal acceptance of precise descriptive criteria will be continued with vigor.

FASHIONS IN DIAGNOSIS

As the description and classification of mental illness has shifted, subdivided, and broadened under the influence of new knowledge, diagnoses have been governed by the interpretations and preferences of individual clinicians and hospitals. This presents the epidemiologist with a second set of variables: as the ground rules have been amended with every play in the game, each player, in an effort to make sense out of an inherently chaotic situation, has placed his own evaluation on the change.

This categorical instability is illustrated by the differences in terminology and apparent weight assigned disease entities by two public mental institutions in Massachusetts, the Boston and Worcester State Hospitals, and by the private McLean Hospital, over a fifty-year period. Table 1 presents the five leading diagnoses upon admission to each of these hospitals at twenty-five-year intervals from 1900 to 1950.

In the three years selected, the five leading diagnoses accounted for anywhere from 42 to 72 per cent of the total and fell within eight general categories: schizophrenia (dementia praecox), manic-depressive psychoses, senile psychoses, alcoholic psychoses, paranoia, general paralysis, involutional psychoses, and psychoses with cerebral arteriosclerosis.

Schizophrenia remained the leading diagnosis upon admission to both the Boston and the Worcester State Hospitals with the exception of 1925. In that year manic-depressive psychosis was the most common diagnosis at Boston (18 per cent), while dementia praecox dropped to 10 per cent. At Worcester, on the other hand, dementia praecox continued to lead the list (20 per cent), and manic-depressive psychosis was

Table 1—Five Leading Diagnoses on Admission to Three Massachusetts Hospitals (1900, 1925, 1950)

Hospital	1900 Diagnosis	Per cent	1925 Diagnosis	Per cent	1950 Diagnosis	Per cent
Boston State Hospital	1. Dementia	19	1. Manic-depressive psychoses	18	1. Dementia praecox	23
	2. Melancholia	10	2. Psychoses with cerebral arteriosclerosis	17	2. Psychoses with cerebral arteriosclerosis	13
	3. Senile insanity	7	3. Senile psychoses	15	3. Alcoholic psychoses	10
	4. Mania, acute	7	4. Dementia praecox	10	4. Senile psychoses	9
	5. Alcoholic insanity	7	5. Alcoholic psychoses	6	5. Manic-depressive psychoses	8
	Totals, 1900	50	Totals, 1925	66	Totals, 1950	63
Worcester State Hospital	1. Dementia praecox	14	1. Dementia praecox	20	1. Dementia praecox	26
	2. Paranoic condition	12	2. Senile	9	2. Psychoses with cerebral arteriosclerosis	10
	3. Alcoholic psychoses	11	3. Psychoses with arteriosclerosis	8	3. Involutional psychoses	7
	4. Senile dementia	8	4. Psychoses with general paralysis	8	4. Manic-depressive psychoses	7
	5. Delirium (infections, toxic and asthenic)	7	5. Manic-depressive	8	5. Alcoholic psychoses	7
	Totals, 1900	52	Totals, 1925	53	Totals, 1950	57
McLean Hospital	1. Depressive maniacal insanity	37	1. Manic-depressive psychoses, depressed	22	1. Psychoneurosis, mixed	12
	2. Dementia praecox	17	2. Manic-depressive psychoses, manic	14	2. Schizophrenia, paranoid	9
	3. General paralysis	9	3. Manic-depressive psychoses, mixed	4	3. Psychoneurosis, reactive depression	8
	4. Involutional psychosis	5	4. Dementia praecox	2	4. Manic-depressive phychoses, manic	8
	5. Senile dementia	4	5. General paralysis	2	5. Involutional melancholia	8
	Totals, 1900	72	Totals, 1925	44	Totals, 1950	45

[26]

fifth (8 per cent). Senile and cerebral arteriosclerotic psychoses were likewise reversed in apparent frequency. It is difficult to believe that the character of admissions to these two institutions in 1925 was as totally different as the diagnoses would indicate.

Comparison with the McLean Hospital during this period is impossible; manic-depressive psychosis was the leading diagnosis in all three years either because of a real difference in the type of patient admitted or because different clinical considerations ruled diagnoses.

By 1950, however, a trend toward uniformity of diagnosis, both descriptively and statistically, is apparent at the two state institutions, although differences in terminology (and, undoubtedly, admissions) remain at McLean.

These data, presenting diagnoses taken twenty-five years apart, cannot be considered conclusive about the types of patients admitted to the three hospitals selected, the incidence of mental illness in the populations they serve, or diagnostic inconsistencies among staff psychiatrists.

They do suggest that historical records of admissions to mental institutions are likely to be of limited value to an epidemiologic survey. Furthermore, to the extent that discrepancies in institutional admitting and diagnostic policies and in the interpretive appraisals of individual psychiatrists continue to distort the record, the evaluation of epidemiologic data will retain a strong element of guesswork.

IV

The Causes of Mental Illness: A Multifactorial Complex

I N VIEW of the difficulties encountered in the description and classification of mental illnesses, it is not unexpected to find that the search for cause has yielded meager results. A few specific agents have been implicated in the etiology of certain types of mental disease. But the mode and extent of their action remain poorly understood, and it can seldom be stated with any assurance that other factors do not interact with or influence a given agent to varying degrees.

THE MOSAIC OF ETIOLOGY

There is every reason to assume that resistance or susceptibility to mental illness is conditioned by the same general classes of host characteristics operating in somatic diseases of multifactorial causation. The first group is composed of genetic factors. The second includes developmental factors under the influence of such variables as age, sex, nutrition, season of the year, and numerous others. The third covers anatomical, physiological, and psychobiological characteristics. The fourth class of host factors encompasses those acquired under stress of the environment—physical, biological, and social—(with the probable exception of antibodies).

The study of the etiology of mass disease proceeds through three units of observation: the cell, subject of histopathology; the individual, subject of clinical pathology; and the group, subject of population pathology, the domain of the epidemiologist (Gordon, 1955).

The causes and mechanisms of disease originate in the characteristics of the cell. Knowledge of etiology begins to be integrated through study of the disease as it appears in the organism. Not until groups of individuals have been analyzed does the causal pattern emerge in its entirety. No one approach is complete in itself; the three are interdependent.

Specific microbiologic and toxic agents are known to produce symptoms of mental disorder by damage or insult to the central nervous system. Mental manifestations have been observed to accompany bacterial infections (for example, tuberculosis, meningitis, whooping cough, and syphilis), viral infections (measles and encephalitis), and certain rickettsial and parasitic diseases. Likewise, mental abnormalities may follow prolonged exposure to toxins such as carbon tetrachloride, carbon monoxide, insecticides, and lead. Doubtless there are many other specific microbiologic and toxic agents of whose participation in etiology we are not yet aware.

There is increasing evidence that biological factors are strongly implicated in the etiology of mental disease. The role of metabolic and hormonal abnormalities and disturbances is only beginning to be suspected. We are no closer than the threshold to this area of investigation.

The same can be said of the genetic role in causality. It has long been appreciated that hereditary factors may predispose certain individuals to some types of mental disease, and it would seem that familial evidence has occasionally given weight to this view. Nevertheless, the causal responsibility of heredity has not been fixed with any certainty, and the most that can be said is that genetically determined characteristics probably make their contribution to mental illness in an infinitely subtle and complex manner.

Beyond the inherent qualities of the individual and the specific agents that may bring about identifiable organic and functional changes in the biological system there exists a bewildering mass of influences from the shadowy realm of the environment. Sometimes an environmental factor, or a group of them, is focused with such intensity on the individual that it is possible to recognize an indisputable causal relationship. A shattering personal relationship, an overwhelming traumatic experience, the cumulative effects of poverty, malnutrition, or role and status responsibility may suddenly—or slowly —appear to upset mental balance. Such influences are necessary, perhaps, but never sufficient for the onset of mental illness, for the adaptation of different individuals to more or less identical environmental pressures ranges from firm resistance to utter submission. The sum of underlying, interacting characteristics of the host is invariably of critical importance.

ADAPTATION AND PERSONALITY

Environmental conditioning commences in the womb and continues through the intimate relationship of mother and child. Strong developmental factors come into play as the child makes increasingly complex adjustments to the challenge of his role in the family. The process of adaptation grows ever more intricate and sophisticated as he faces the demands upon his personality of education, adolescence, marriage, and of parental, economic, and social responsibility.

The mental health of the individual depends on his ability to make the adjustments consistent with social living, at the same time preserving the integrity of his personality. If social scientists will forgive a simple metaphor, we might say that the personality is the imperfect dike constructed from heritage and environment that must hold back the waters of anxiety, frustration and guilt, whatever their source. Groups and populations, too, have their personality dikes, as witness the retention of the customs of the old country by minority groups, the protective regulations of professional associations, fraternal organizations, and labor unions, and the determination with which the southern states oppose racial integration.

CAUSE AND ECOLOGY

The Indians of Peru learned how to suppress the symptoms of malaria with quinine-containing cinchona bark more than three centuries ago. But it was not until Ronald Ross found in 1897–1898 that the *Anopheles* mosquito is the carrier of the malarial parasite *Plasmodium* that the etiology of the infection was finally understood. Malaria was seen as the result of a three-way ecologic relationship between man, parasite, and mosquito, and epidemiology was able to aim prevention and control at the real villain—the mosquito.

Mental illness is probably the supreme example of ecology

at work, and the very fact that so much of it is the product of the interaction between man and his environment suggests that the epidemiologist need not throw up his hands in the face of the etiologic dilemma. *Plasmodium* had been discovered and its life cycle described years before Ross proved *Anopheles* to be its vector. It is worth while remembering that he did so only by going into the field and chasing mosquitos. Likewise, the significance of painstaking clinical and laboratory investigations of mental disease will never fully be appreciated nor the totality of its cause grasped until they have been correlated with field observations of man in his environment.

Admittedly, malaria has been a recognized clinical entity since the time of Hippocrates. But even here the analogy retains an element of relevance. The treatment of malaria was empirical and symptomatic, notwithstanding its clinical autonomy, until mosquito control programs began to strike at the mass disease. The current treatment of mental illness is also empirical and symptomatic, at least to a very high degree, and will probably remain so until the cause behind the effect has been recognized. Needless to say, the study of each contributes to an understanding of the other—cause and effect, agent and disease.

The epidemiologist, by coordinating the endeavors of all sciences that are qualified to shed light on the problem, is in a position to organize a new, ecologically oriented approach to the etiology of mental illness. Such a multidisciplined inspection may turn out to be infinitely more comprehensive than the sum of its separate parts.

V

Is Mental Disturbance Communicable?

F OR MANY years psychologists, psychiatrists, and social scientists have been intrigued by the recurrent proposition that mental disturbances, under certain unusual circumstances, are communicable. History is sprinkled with countless examples of individual and group irrationality that cannot be explained by the usual standards of mental pathology. Time and again, the evidence seemed to suggest that these aberrations—often attaining the proportions (in their manifestations, at least) of frank mental illness—were actually communicated during the course of bizarre and unaccountable relationships. The hypothesis is an attractive one, but it lacks the support of indisputable scientific documentation.

Perhaps the strongest foundation for the hypothesis of communicability is to be found in the family relationship, where the personality and environmental adjustments of the developing child are shaped both vertically and horizontally by those

with whom he comes in closest contact. Fears, emotional
tension, and perhaps even mental illness are transmitted from
parent to offspring, from generation to generation. It is well
established that a parent may "act out" with the child—often
in a highly oblique and obscure fashion—the stresses and
abnormal relationships to which he had been subjected as a
child.

Hypnosis and religious conversion may involve the com-
munication of irrationality by means of powerful and perhaps
pathological personal relationships. Examples of "transference
cures" as a result of personality dominance during psycho-
therapy have been noted, and the same kind of one-sided relationship appears to be responsible for the appearance of
iatrogenic disorders in patients who fancy they suffer from
heart disease, cancer, or other ailments in response to the
highly-charged suggestive power of their physicians. Finally,
there is the dual psychosis of *folie à deux,* a grotesque phenomenon in which the psychiatric symptoms of one individual
are communicated to, and reflected by, another over a long
period of close association.

On a group level, panic can be interpreted as aggregate
irrationality communicated among individuals under the influence of stress. There have been a number of documented
instances of mass hallucination, and nations have been in-
duced by propaganda and mass persuasion to act irrationally
and to approve the irrational acts of others to an extent that
may approach national psychosis. The anxieties, frustrations,
and intergroup conflicts of society since time immemorial
have found an outlet in the search for scapegoats and stereo-
types; this relentless pressure of hostility and disapproval has
had profound effect on the attitudes of the outcasts toward

themselves and others, whether they were Jews, Negroes, pariahs, immigrants, or the mentally ill.

However, all irrationality (or distortion of reality) is not mental illness, though it may be one characteristic of it. No one is consistently rational in his behavior and thought processes, nor is he entirely immune to mental disturbance. The degree to which each individual has adjusted to his life situation is a key factor in his mental health.

It is not suggested, of course, that mental illness (or disturbance) is communicated through specific agents in the way that infectious diseases are transmitted in groups of individuals and populations. Nor do we mean to imply that every environmental influence to which the individual is exposed is *per se* communicable. A communicable disease is one that is capable of being transmitted from one person to another. In the absence of a specific communicable agent of mental disease, it may be postulated that mental disturbance can be "projected" from one individual to another. Mental health may be equally communicable, for that matter, by the parent, the educator, the leader, the clergyman, and the psychotherapist (Milton Golin, 1959).

Whether frank mental illness is transmitted, if at all, is open to question. The existence of such clinical phenomena as *folie à deux,* and the rather strong evidence of a chain of transmission in the family, suggest that the hypothesis warrants further investigation within the context of epidemiology. Sick ideas and healthy ideas, socially useful values and antisocial values, are indeed communicable and have an important place among the many elements contributing to a picture of mental health or illness in the individual and in the population.

Mental illness emerges from a baffling wilderness of causes.

The clinical reaction may be so low-grade or atypical as not to be recognizable among known forms of discrete disease entities. Predisposing factors may spring from a genetic background out of which issued the organic and functional complex that brought about subclinical metabolic changes in the central nervous system. The gun thus loaded may never be fired. Or it may be triggered by a succession of environmental influences beginning in infancy—all of them, indeed, "communicated" along pathways whose source and outline are yet but suspected.

VI

Secondhand Information: The Secondary Source

T HE EPIDEMIOLOGIST initially views the gross problem of mental illness from afar, and as he inspects its large dimensions he aims to measure its prevalence numerically. By introducing estimates of incidence he gets an over-all picture of its temporal, geographic, and demographic distributions in the population.

This information is of little value in itself, however. Practical public health measures directed toward prevention and control proceed from a combination of general principles and specific, applicable facts about causation. This calls for a detailed inspection of the problem in depth.

First, the total amount of treated mental illness is measured, and a series of questions are posed. What kinds of mental illness are being treated, and by whom? Is there a correlation between treatment and severity of disease? How intense is treatment? How long does it last? How effective is it?

Finally, the bulk of untreated mental illness is estimated. What kinds of mental illness are escaping treatment? Are there qualitative differences between treated and untreated disease? What standards should be applied to determine the type and severity of illness that warrant treatment? Which facilities should be handling cases that are missing treatment? Where and who are the untreated patients, and how are they to be found and brought to therapy?

Some of these questions extend in their implications beyond the immediate interest of the epidemiologist, but they are nonetheless crucial to a definition of the total problem; throughout them, of course, runs the recurring question of etiology.

The difficulties facing the epidemiologist are compounded by the necessity to leap into the middle of the ideal continuum of investigation for information upon which to predicate an evaluation of the whole. Thus the investigator cannot define the total problem until he has first succeeded in estimating with reasonable accuracy the amount of treated mental illness. This implies that he must start in the middle, directing his attention initially to treated illness in recognized institutions, then proceeding backward toward a more general appreciation of total numbers receiving treatment from a variety of sources, and forward toward a study of the untreated segment.

A realistic measurement of treated mental illness in the United States is difficult to achieve at best. Because the treated rate is dominated by the availability and caliber of treatment facilities and by the attitudes of the individual and the community toward mental illness and treatment, it is a poor index of prevalence. If the treatment rate (and this includes the noninstitutionalized who receive treatment informally or sporadically) could be defined with accuracy, it is apparent that the untreated rate would be the key determinant of general prevalence.

Nevertheless, the diagnostic criteria by which untreated mental illness—and, inferentially, the gross problem—is to be defined must be derived largely from the study of that segment of the total that is closest to hand and most readily identifiable, the treated cases. What are the available data on persons under treatment for mental illness? How reliable is the information?

SOURCES OF INFORMATION

Data can be separated into two general classes: secondary sources, which include hospitals, social agencies, courts, and other institutions concerned directly or indirectly with mental illness problems, the Selective Service System and Armed Forces, and the so-called "nonprofessional informant"; and community surveys, "grass roots" sources of firsthand information that use direct case-finding techniques. The community surveys will be discussed at some length in Chapter VII.

Secondary sources possess the common drawback of yielding information compiled under widely varying circumstances over which the investigator had no control.

Mental Hospital Records

The records of mental hospitals have provided the statistical material for most of the epidemiologic studies of treated mental illness in the United States.

Herbert Goldhamer and Andrew Marshall (1953) used hospital statistics from 1840 to 1940 to investigate the long-range trend in incidence of committable psychoses in Massachusetts. Horatio M. Pollock (1941) reprinted in one volume a number of his previously published articles based on mental hospital data. This book contained statistical analyses of the incidence of various mental disorders according to age and sex, the expectation of disorders among various population groups, and hospital release rates for specified groups. Benjamin Malzberg (1940) published a group of studies of the distribution of patients in mental institutions in New York State and the relationship of admissions and diagnoses to variables of age, sex, race, nativity, and socio-economic status.

Carney Landis and James Page (1938) investigated mental disease as measured by mental hospital data in relation to such social factors as age, urbanization, race, social level, and marital status. The data included comparative information from several countries. Neil Dayton (1940) studied the characteristics of all patients admitted to Massachusetts mental hospitals during the years 1919 to 1933. This was one of the earlier investigations of trends in mental illness prevalence and incidence as reflected in mental hospital population and admissions.

Robert Faris and H. Warren Dunham (1939) studied the relation of hospitalized psychoses by diagnostic group to socio-economic areas of several cities. Ornulv Odegard (1932) sought to use commitment as a measure of disease severity among migrant and nonmigrant populations. Robert Clark (1949) investigated hospitalization rates in relation to income and occupational prestige.

These and many other surveys have been based on hospital records, and doubtless institutional statistics will continue to have an important place in epidemiologic research in this field. The evaluation of therapy, for instance, must rely heavily on hospital data.

We have already indicated some of the defects in this approach; the criticism by Robert H. Felix and Robert V. Bowers (1948, pp. 127–128) of the mental hospital as a source of information applies generally to all secondary sources:

> The researchers have no control over the case-finding process, over the record keeping, or even the diagnosis. Rather, they are dependent upon the public's uneven willingness to give up its mentally ill members and to support them in institutions, the hospital's unstandardized record-keeping activities, and the hospital staffs' varied training and skill in classifying disorders.

It has been estimated that 1,070,000 Americans are hospitalized for mental illness in federal, state, and private institutions and in the psychiatric units of general hospitals. Approximately 30 per cent of those annually admitted have been hospitalized at least once previously for a mental illness. About one third of the first admissions are over fifty-five years old.

Another 379,000 patients, at least, are treated in mental health clinics; between 365,000 and 451,000 are seen in the offices of psychiatrists. Estimates of psychiatric patients attended by physicians other than psychiatrists range from about 10 to 70 per cent of the total. It is not known how many medical patients are seen in consultation by psychiatrists or are referred to mental hospitals where they show up again in their census figures. Nor is there any estimate of the number of mentally ill who consult the clergy, psychologists, and social agencies.

Because the adequacy of hospital facilities varies throughout the United States, hospitalization rates tend to reflect mainly the use and extent of facilities. The rates are clearly a more accurate index of severe than of mild illnesses, and are far from representative. Not all severe cases are treated, of course. Moreover, statistical data have been drawn more generally and are more readily available from public mental institutions than from all hospitals, public and private, having facilities for the treatment or care of the mentally ill.

The limitations that apply to prevalence and incidence data hold also for the second broad epidemiologic use of hospital statistics; namely, the search for causative and determining factors of mental illness. Hospital populations are selected populations. The restricted value of these data has been emphasized. The number of admissions reflects community attitudes toward deviant behavior and the availability of hospital beds, rather than prevalence in the community. Despite these reservations, hospital data are probably more useful than any others as an index of the broad demographic relationships of mental disorders. They have less value as measures of the innate characteristics of the human host presumably active in the genesis of mental disease. Insofar as severe mental illness is concerned, certain generalizations emerge.

Female patients outnumber males, and frequency of attack increases with age. Marital status is clearly associated with occurrence of mental disease; the unmarried are more susceptible than the married, and the widowed and divorced have high attack rates. Race and nativity are suggestive determining factors (in recent years, hospital admission rates of Negroes in the United States have exceeded those of whites, a shift probably related more to altered social conditions than to race). Residents of rural areas tend to have more mental disorders than do urbanites. Migration within a country and between countries appears to contribute to the frequency of psychosis and other mental disorders. Variations in the economic welfare of a society influence frequency of mental disease to the extent, at least, that admissions to mental hospitals increase during times of financial stress.

Although such observations are not applicable with certainty to general populations or to causality, they provide significant leads toward the direction of controlled investigation.

The Socially Visible Case

Many of the mentally ill, because of their social or economic status or the mildness or inoffensiveness of their symptoms, do not come to the attention of community agencies and institutions. In their study of New Haven, August Hollingshead and Frederick Redlich (1958), found that lower-income patients tended to receive only custodial care and organic treatment, whereas the services of the private psychiatrist were largely reserved for members of the middle- and higher-income brackets. In all probability, exclusive reliance on community agencies and institutions in epidemiologic surveys results in bias in the direction of the lower-income groups. In the 1936 study of Baltimore's Eastern Health District (Paul Lemkau et al., 1941, 1942a, 1942b, 1943), the research group suggested that the lower-income brackets were overrepresented in the cases obtained from clinics and social agencies, although canvassing of both private and public mental hospitals resulted in accurate representation from all groups of psychotics in need of institutional care. In order to get a measure of their coverage, they worked out an index of case-finding and found, as they expected, that their canvass was more complete for the less privileged. This index, however, applied only to those defined as psychotic, adult neurotic, and epileptic.

An early survey of Nassau County in New York (Aaron Rosanoff, 1917) supports the point that some of the mentally ill escape the attention of the community because of the low social visibility of their symptoms. The study director believed his findings underestimated the true state of affairs, partly because many cases of abnormality that were of lesser significance from the sociological standpoint were undoubtedly missed. The leads to possible cases of mental disorder as provided by secondary sources were almost exclusively sociological (behavior problems such as truancy or drunkenness); an individual in whom these problems were not present and whose symptoms were of low social visibility was not likely to be recognized.

The significance of the special interests and reporting activities of the particular agency is illustrated by the 1933 study of the Eastern Health District in Baltimore (Bernard Cohen *et al.*, 1938a, 1938b, 1939a, 1939b). It was the impression of the research group (1939a) that the social agency serving the Jews of the district paid special attention to personality problems. Identified cases thus may have been more nearly complete for Jews than for non-Jews.

Nonpsychiatrically oriented informants comprise another type of secondary source sometimes used in surveys—persons who are consulted because of their wide contacts or familiarity with individuals in the community. These include old residents, clergymen, and district nurses. This source, too, probably results in a considerable underenumeration of the milder, inoffensive forms of mental disorder. Such informants usually are alert only to gross symptomatology.

War-Born Information

The massive screening of the male population by the Selective Service System during two world wars, together with discharge rates of members of the Armed Forces for psychiatric reasons, are a ready-made source of data for the epidemiologist. These statistics on neuropsychiatric conditions provide an insight into the general prevalence of mental illness different from other secondary sources and must be interpreted with caution.

Leonard G. Rowntree, Kenneth H. McGill, and Louis P. Hellman (1945) reported that mental and personality disorders were the most important causes of rejection of white registrants during World War II; among Negroes they were surpassed only by mental deficiency and syphilis. They were also the leading causes of discharge for disability from the Armed Forces. Rejection rates for mental and personality disorders, however, varied through the war years. About 24 per 1000 examinees were rejected for these reasons in 1940 and 1941, a figure that rose to 67 in 1942 and 1943 and to 120 in 1944. Some of the increase may be attributed to increased tension as the war progressed, but additional factors were also at work. The lowering of standards in other defect categories produced an apparent increase in psychiatric rejection rates. Standards for dental and visual abnormalities were lowered in 1942; this enhanced the likelihood of rejection for psychiatric reasons, because a number of registrants who might have been turned down for the more obvious defects of teeth and eyes also suffered mental or personality disorders.

Furthermore, there were wide differences among induction stations in the efficiency and technique of psychiatric screening. The training and experience of neuropsychiatric personnel and their ratio to selectees varied. According to William A. Hunt and Cecil L. Wittson (1949, p. 353): ". . . many military psychiatrists were general medicine men 'converted' by short training courses, and . . . often in the absence of a psychiatrist a general practitioner had to function in a psychiatric capacity. . . ."

Hunt and Wittson (p. 355) cited another source of error in psychiatric screening:

A specific psychiatrist or local psychiatric unit may be predisposed toward the use of certain diagnostic categories and the neglect of others. Thus the final diagnosis in any particular instance may be a function of the diagnostic prejudice of the particular psychiatrist examining the patient rather than a direct function of the specific symptomatology actually present.

Examiners at induction stations worked at great speed and under heavy pressure and without the benefit of complete case studies, conditions that increased the chance of rejecting the fit and accepting the unfit. Deliberate distortions of diagnosis were often made for humane or administrative reasons, and physical defects were assigned to individuals in order to relieve them of the stigma of a neuropsychiatric discharge.

Any attempt to extrapolate prevalence rates from these statistics must take into consideration voluntary enlistees who bypassed Selective Service screening. Varying prevalence rates, too, may be related to changes in the ages of registrants; during 1940 and 1941 the ages of those examined were mainly twenty-one to thirty-five years, twenty to forty-four in 1942 and eighteen to thirty-seven in 1943 and 1944 (Rowntree,

McGill, and Hellman, 1945). Finally, many men were automatically deferred for dependency or occupational reasons.

Throughout the war period the nature and duration of stress situations varied widely, a variable further complicated by the marked difference between the military environment and the normal patterns of civilian life. The records of neuropsychiatric disorders of World War II are to be interpreted with caution, bearing in mind, above all, that they apply almost exclusively to adult males eligible for military service. They are not relevant to women or children, to men too young or too old to serve, or to those deferred for physical, dependency, or occupational reasons.

In short, the "population" to which these data refer was a transient grouping brought together under extraordinary conditions and the exigencies of a national emergency. As a population, it was artificial; it did not exist before the war, and it does not exist now.

VII

Firsthand Information:
The Community Survey

T HE COMMUNITY is a source of firsthand information about the ecology of health and disease. As a starting point for epidemiologic investigation of mental illness, it has the advantage of reducing the scope of the inquiry to manageable proportions. Although the truly representative community probably does not exist, the carefully chosen group or sample can produce significant leads under conditions of careful research and analysis.

Most community surveys of mental illness have been studies of populations whose limits were established by political or geographical boundaries. A few have been confined to strongly homogeneous groups. The object of a study design is to establish uniform and fixed methods of investigation, a standard fact-finding procedure, and an adequate staff, all consistent with available resources.

Because the epidemiologic approach to mental illness has

placed much emphasis on the community survey, we have analyzed 11 representative studies conducted in the forty-two-year interval between 1916 and 1958. Their orientation, personnel, populations considered, criteria of mental illness, case-finding techniques, and diagnostic categories are compared. No two have followed identical lines. The inconsistency of results is largely because each study has itself introduced an extrinsic variable between its findings and true prevalence.

The purpose of the present analysis is to explore the nature of these procedural variables in the hope that this will contribute to the search for better principles of study design in the future. The 11 studies are outlined briefly in Table 2.

THE QUESTION

The strongest clue to the general nature of a particular community survey is the question it asks. The conclusions that follow are based on an analysis of answers given by different people in different places at different times under different conditions in response to different questioners. The key variable—the one that conditions, to one degree or another, all the others—is the nature of the question. The questions asked by the eleven surveys may be divided among eight categories.

1. *What kinds of and how much chronic illness is there in the community?*

Not all of the studies were intended primarily as surveys of mental illness. The Commission on Chronic Illness studies in Maryland (1957) and New Jersey (Ray E. Trussell and Jack Elinson) gained information about mental illness in the course of a broad investigation of chronic illness in general and then related the findings to age, sex, color, and income.

Table 2—Eleven Community Surveys of Mental Illness (1916–1958)

Survey	Year	Field of Interest	Authors and Publication Dates
Nassau County, N. Y.	1916	Social maladjustment due to mental illness	Rosanoff, A. J. (1917)
Eastern Health District, Baltimore, Md.	1933	Socially evident mental illness	Cohen, B. M. et al. (1938a, 1938b, 1939a, 1939b)
Eastern Health District, Baltimore, Md.	1936	Socially evident mental illness	Lemkau, P. et al. (1941, 1941a, 1942, 1943)
Williamson County, Tenn.	1935–1938	Candidates for mental illness treatment	Roth, W. F., Luton, F. H. (1943)
Hutterite Communities, Dakotas, Montana, and Alberta, Canada	1950	The way of life and resistance to mental illness	Eaton, J. W., Weil, R. J. (1955)
Hunterdon County, N. J.	1951–1955	All chronic illness (including institutionalized)	Trussell, R. E., Elinson, J. (1959)
Baltimore, Md.	1953–1955	Noninstitutionalized chronic illness	Commission on Chronic Illness (1957)
Salt Lake City, Utah	1955	Diagnosable mental illness	Cole, Nyla J., Branch, C. H. H., Shaw, Orla M. (1957)
Syracuse, N. Y.	1955	Marital status and mental illness in the aged	Bellin, S. S., Hardt, R. H. (1958)
Syracuse, N. Y.	1955	Socio-economic status, sex, and mental illness in the aged	Downing, J. J., Gruenberg, E. M. (1957)
Midtown Manhattan, N. Y.	1952–1958	Sociocultural factors and mental illness	Rennie, T. A. C., Srole, L., Langner, T., Opler, M. (in press)

Surveys designed to answer questions of this nature can provide useful information for planning community health programs. In fact, an important objective of the Commission studies was to assess the potential for rehabilitation and the needs for care of the chronically disabled, including the mentally ill, in the communities surveyed.

General illness surveys can be used to compare roughly the prevalence of mental and physical diseases, although absence of a main psychiatric orientation limits observations to the more obvious instances of mental illness. These studies do not claim complete, accurate assessment of mental illness prevalence.

2. *How much mental illness has come to the attention of community institutions and agencies?*

The studies of the Eastern Health District in Baltimore counted individuals under the care of agencies and institutions dealing with mental hygiene problems, including public and private mental hospitals and clinics, training schools for mental defectives and delinquents, social service agencies, certain departments of public school systems, and the courts.

The findings were governed by the nature and functions of the agencies and institutions canvassed and by the extent to which they were used by individuals in the community.

3. *How much social maladjustment, sufficiently marked to have come to the attention of the public authorities, can be attributed mainly to mental disorder?*

This question motivated Rosanoff's survey of Nassau County in 1916. The answer, like that to the previous question, depended on the particular interests of the agencies and institutions studied and on the extent of their use.

4. *How many persons in the community on any given day*

should be under the care of a mental hygiene clinic or mental hospital.

William F. Roth and Frank H. Luton (1943) sought to locate in a rural county of Tennessee all those who would be eligible for referral to a clinic, hospital, or other institution dealing with mental hygiene problems. They enumerated individuals regarded by others as suitable candidates in addition to those located through an intensive door-to-door survey.

5. *How much recognizable mental illness is there in the community?*

Nyla J. Cole, C. H. Hardin Branch, and Orla M. Shaw (1957) computed the percentage of individuals in their Salt Lake City sample with overt symptomatology or admission of mental illness. They noted the amount of treatment received and analyzed attitudes toward the desirability of treatment.

6. *Does a certain way of life protect against mental disorder?*

In order to test the hypothesis that the simple way of life of the Hutterites, a German Anabaptist sect in the Dakotas, Montana, and Alberta, renders them less susceptible to mental illness, Joseph W. Eaton and Robert J. Weil (1955) searched for all cases of mental disorder known to have occurred among living members of the group and compared their findings with information derived from other populations.

7. *What is the relationship of certain variables to mental illness in nonhospitalized persons aged sixty-five years or over?*

Seymour S. Bellin and Robert H. Hardt (1958) investigated the relationship between marital status (primarily the married and widowed) and mental disorder in the aged. Joseph J. Downing and Ernest M. Gruenberg (1957) correlated age over sixty-five, socio-economic status, and sex to frequency of mental illness.

8. *How do sociocultural factors in childhood and adulthood affect mental health?*

The purpose of the long-range Midtown Mental Health Survey in New York City by Thomas Rennie, Leo Srole, Thomas Langner, and Marvin Opler was to test the hypothesis that causality of mental illness is multifactorial. A random sample of residents in a densely populated section of Manhattan with a wide range of socio-economic levels was examined in relation to eight variables.

The question any study seeks to answer evidently sets the stage for the entire production. Study planners must know what to ask and how to ask it in order to obtain answers that can be evaluated. A number of skills are required both in the asking and in the analyzing. The qualifications of personnel are of crucial importance.

THE PERSONNEL

The particular skills required of personnel in surveys of a population are determined primarily by the nature of the investigation and the characteristics of the population under study. Examination of the field studies under consideration shows that the value of the several possible scientific disciplines has not been definitely established in practice.

The currently favored concept of multidisciplinary team research is attractive on the face of it but often unsatisfactory in application. Group investigation is more apt to bear fruit when the members of the team are representatives of the same discipline than when they bring to it on an equal footing different scientific backgrounds with divergent viewpoints and approaches. General direction of the study and implementation of agreed policies rests to advantage with some one worker, qualified by training and experience for the task at hand. When skilled workers in other disciplines participate, they should be permitted to develop their parts of the program individually; but one person must put the pieces together.

The group endeavor is most useful during the preliminary or planning stages of a project. An initial meeting of minds can be of value in constructing a conceptual framework and in coordinating lines of investigation.

Basic research, however, must remain to a very large degree an individual responsibility. All scientific study, regardless of the complexity of its subject matter, boils down in the final analysis to individual creativity. The coordination of the work of various scientists participating in any study as complex as that concerned with mental illness is plainly essential; overall planning, division of labor, and intercommunication are all to the good. But it must be borne in mind that the aggregate accomplishments of any team are measured in terms of the individual efforts of its members, and epidemiologic research is no exception.

Nassau County

The director was a physician with extensive psychiatric training. The staff included four physicians with some psychiatric experience, a psychologist, and 15 college-trained female field workers who had either courses or experience in areas related to social work. The field workers interviewed each individual referred for suspected mental abnormality; they also interviewed his relatives. Weekly staff conferences discussed specific cases. Final decisions as to the existence of mental abnormality, and its diagnosis, were based on data gathered in the field survey, always in consultation with the director or assistant director. Two of the physicians investigated cases in the field and supervised field workers. Another was in the field part time. The fourth examined patients in institutions. Investigation of cases of possible abnormality among school-age children was conducted by physicians from the United States Public Health Service.

Eastern Health District (1933 and 1936)

Both studies were under the direction of a medical statistician, a psychiatrist, and a social worker. No information is given about the specific tasks of each. The studies depended on descriptive and diagnostic information from community members, including psychiatrists, social workers, court personnel, law enforcement officers, and school teachers. Apparently the authors of the study reports were jointly responsible for collection, review and classification of data, as well as initial study design.

Tennessee

The study was initiated by two psychiatrists. They were assisted by two social workers and a psychiatric nurse, each of whom studied one third of the county and investigated referred cases of possible mental disorder. The director also did field work, particularly in an intensive survey of one part of the county, and met with key people in the area. The consultant-codirector made occasional field trips and participated in the weekly staff conferences. Apparently the field workers had primary responsibility for separating the well from the mentally ill.

Hutterite Communities

This group was headed by a sociologist, assisted by a psychiatrist. The staff included two psychologists, five field-work research assistants with varying terms of employment, and a research assistant. The field-work research assistants were graduate students, most of them with a background in sociology. The psychiatrist and four other physicians were consultants in the preparation of a check list used to obtain information about the Hutterites from physicians who had treated members of the group. All physical examinations were made by the psychiatrist. It is not stated who gave psychological tests. Field workers interviewed Hutterites who were referred as possibly mentally ill, as well as individuals in the community considered "good informants." All diagnoses were by the psychiatrist in consultation with the sociologist. Weekly staff conferences were held.

New Jersey

The study was headed by a physician who was director of the Hunterdon Medical Center, and by a social scientist who was a senior study director of the National Opinion Research Center; both are now on the staff of the School of Public Health and Administrative Medicine, Columbia University. Household interviews were conducted, it was stated, by 35 "trained" interviewers. Evaluation teams included a physician, a medical social worker (or psychiatric social worker with medical social work training and experience), and a public health nurse with "advanced training in mental health." They examined a selected sample of those interviewed. Two internists and a pediatrician did the examinations for the evaluation teams. A specialist in obstetrics and gynecology did pelvic examinations on all women. A full array of specialists, including a psychiatrist and clinical psychologist, was available for consultations. The pediatrician was said to be psychiatrically oriented, but not the internists. Each member of the team reviewed and evaluated all data about each individual and participated in a joint decision about the kind and amount of disability. The physician had final clinical decision as to the presence or absence of disease.

Baltimore

The United States Bureau of the Census had major responsibility for the household interviews which were designed and field-tested under contract to the Commission on Chronic Illness. Representatives of the Bureau of the Census also selected the sample to be used, conducted interviews, and tabulated the findings. A biostatistician was consulted on several aspects of the study, particularly sampling methods. An evaluation clinic was staffed by a panel of physicians specializing either in internal medicine or in pediatrics, a medical social worker, and a rehabilitation counselor. The diagnoses of mental illness were by the internists, with or without psychiatric consultation or psychometric testing. Medical records were later reviewed by a psychiatrist who classified cases by diagnosis and severity of impairment.

Salt Lake City

A third-year psychiatric resident, a psychiatrist, and a psychiatric social worker conducted this survey. Interviews and recognition of mental illness were made by the resident physician and the social worker. There is no information about interview technique or other persons involved in study design or administration.

Syracuse

These two studies of elderly people were part of a study by the New York State Mental Health Research Unit. The director of the Unit was a clinical psychiatrist trained in the epidemiology of mental illness and experienced in community organization. The permanent study staff included two psychiatrists, two epidemiologists, two sociologists, a social psychologist, a clinical psychologist, a psychiatric social worker, a public health nurse, two biostatisticians, and two research assistants. Temporary field workers were employed from time to time for collection of data and other special duties.

The study of marital status was conducted by the associate sociologist and a research assistant. They consulted a psychiatrist, a psychiatric social worker, and a clinical psychologist in diagnostic evaluation of the material collected. They did not state who conducted the interviews. The differential study of the aged was made by two psychiatrists of the Unit, one the Director (Gruenberg). Apparently they did not do the interviewing themselves.

Midtown

The Manhattan survey was directed by a social psychiatrist. A research team representing clinical psychiatry, clinical psychology, sociology, anthropology, psychiatric social work, and biostatistics spent a year in determining the conceptual and procedural framework. Construction of the interview questionnaire required fourteen months. Interviewers were a specially trained group experienced in free-style methods of interviewing. All data were evaluated independently by staff psychiatrists under supervision of the director.

CASE - FINDING

Specific cases are the raw materials of the community survey. The objectives of the study determine the method used to locate them. Cases may be chosen either indirectly from secondary sources or directly by means of psychiatric screening or household interviews. A combination of these approaches often is employed.

Although exclusive reliance on secondary sources, as already emphasized, will not result in a true value for either prevalence or incidence of mental illness in a population, means exist for getting an approximation of the residue of uncovered cases. Some surveys based on secondary sources subsequently selected subdivisions of the population for intensive house-to-house investigation. The results thus obtained were compared with the rates derived from the secondary sources alone.

Psychiatric screening has been used to locate cases and to verify the results of other case-finding techniques. Many investigators consider this the most reliable research instrument, because a population sample is examined directly. The technique requires trained psychiatrists; it is time-consuming, and expensive. It predicates cooperation of the subject and validity of the sample.

The third case-finding technique, the household interview, raises three questions: Who does the interviewing? What kind of questionnaire and interviewing technique does he use? Does he personally see every member of the family, or are some of his data based on information about one member supplied by another?

The household interview generally affords a fleeting opportunity to identify a mental disease. Hence, only the grosser forms of mental illness are usually recognized; milder disorders require an exceptionally perceptive and experienced interviewer.

Interviews range from superficial questionnaires to "depth probing," an attempt to go beyond verbal expression to underlying emotions and attitudes. If the interviewer uses a schedule (a set of questions asked of every respondent in the same order), some standardization of data is gained, but depth may be sacrificed. Reliability and significance of the information depend on the skill with which the questionnaire is constructed and on proper interviewing technique.

The more flexible interview guide (a list of points or topics the interviewer plans to cover) allows greater freedom. The questioner has leeway to probe when responses are vague or contradictory. Some of the probe questions may place an emotional burden on the respondent, and the field worker must be able to offer support and understanding for the sake of continued cooperation. The less formal nature of the interview makes standardization of data more difficult and the technique of recording answers proportionately more crucial.

The competence of the interviewer and a subtlety of method are called to the test when he is faced with distinguishing between bona fide mental illness and transitory symptoms arising from unusual conditions of stress. Without a psychiatric background and an opportunity to probe in depth, it is doubtful whether most interviewers can differentiate between the two. When the contributions of dispositional weakness and environmental stress to symptomatology are complementary, the challenge to an interviewer is even more formidable.

The field worker does not always have opportunity to talk with all occupants of a home. How reliable is information about one member of the household when supplied by another?

Comparing results of a comprehensive family interview with the findings of a thorough clinical examination, the Hunterdon County investigators observed that underreporting was more of a problem than overreporting. They concluded that mental, personality, and psychoneurotic disorders, as established by clinical examination, were more likely to turn up in the household interview when the individual reported for himself than when the report was by others of the family.

Marian R. Yarrow *et al.* (1955) found that wives were generally unwilling or unable to perceive mental illness in their husbands, tending to rationalize the apparent deviant behavior of the spouse.

All household members were not seen personally by the Salt Lake City group. The prevalence of mental disorder appeared to be higher among women than men, a finding ascribed to the circumstance that only women were at home when the interviewer called. In order to test ability to perceive mental illness, respondents were provided with clinical descriptions of paranoia and neurosis. Thirty-five per cent of those interviewed considered the case of paranoia as relatively normal, and 59.4 per cent thought it serious; the example of neurosis was regarded as relatively normal by 39 per cent, and as serious by 46.3 per cent. This further indicates a tendency to normalize deviant behavior.

As might be expected, most of the community surveys found it necessary to use a combination of case-finding techniques. Four, however (the Salt Lake City study, the two in Syracuse, and the Midtown study), relied on the household interview. The nature of the interview varied considerably among these studies.

Salt Lake City

Eight separate city blocks were selected for study, with 25 consecutive families to be interviewed in each. The total sample included 200 families, of which 175 cooperated; the authors believed a higher rate of discernible mental illness probably existed in the remaining 25. Initially, each family received an introductory letter associating the survey with a research project at the University of Utah College of Medicine. Unstructured personal interviews moved from general queries about child rearing and medical care to more pointed psychiatric questions. The authors suggested that mental illness attributed to absent family members may have been colored by the psychopathology of the respondent. The authors arrived at a prevalence rate of approximately 333 per 1000 for all mental disorders in persons over sixteen years of age.

Syracuse

Bellin and Hardt interviewed about 88 per cent of 1803 persons sixty-five years of age and over and living in six census tracts selected from among those with extreme rates of hospitalization for patients with psychoses of old age. The interviews followed a schedule of topics and inventories about social history, the subjective feelings of the respondent, and the state of physical and mental health. Each symptom relating to mental health was rated on a five-point scale. Later, an independent evaluation of individual mental health was made by a psychiatrist, a psychologist, and a psychiatric social worker. A prevalence rate of 232 per 1000 was obtained for all mental disorders among persons sixty-five years of age and over.

Downing and Gruenberg's staff completed interviews with 1534 persons from six census tracts, all of them over sixty-five years of age. Sixty institutionalized residents were not included, and 200 others were omitted because of incomplete interviews due to impaired mental functioning. The authors agreed that this resulted in underenumeration. The rate of 53 per 1000 for all mental disorders in this age group was substantially less than in the previous study, apparently because that study also included the milder disorders.

Midtown

Case-finding was through highly structured and concentrated household interviews, requiring an average of two hours to complete, but sometimes running to four. The questionnaire included 200 items concerned with demographic and situational factors during childhood and adulthood thought to be related to current mental status, along with 120 items having to do with behavioral or intrapsychic symptoms. The investigators appreciated that achievement of standardization sacrificed to some extent spontaneity in response, but the scope of the survey made free-style interviewing impractical. Psychiatric diagnosis was based on interview material plus four other kinds of data: (1) free associations and asides of the respondent; (2) observations of his behavior during the interview; (3) information from patient census files on psychiatric treatment during the span of the census; and (4) data from the New York Social Service Index.

Calculated prevalence was 233 per 1000 for a group called "impaired," and judged generally equivalent in range of pathology to the total mental disorder group studied by the Commission on Chronic Illness in Baltimore. The Midtown impaired rate applies only to the Midtown sample's age range of twenty to fifty-nine.

The Nassau County, Hutterite, and Tennessee surveys combined secondary source investigation with direct examination or interview.

Nassau County

The first stage of the investigation was directed toward securing leads to possible cases of mental abnormality from provisional lists provided by secondary sources. An attempt then was made to obtain data on these cases sufficient to establish an abnormality and to give some indication of its nature. Referred individuals and their near relatives were investigated, and many were found to be normal. Most of the leads were sociological; the authors concluded that they missed many cases not manifesting gross behavior problems, as well as some that did. Accordingly, they selected four districts for intensive household interviews. The intensive survey uncovered numerous cases not presenting social problems, but these districts were judged to have more disturbed behavior than the county at large; they included some notoriously bad neighborhoods. A prevalence rate of 36.4 per 1000 was established for all mental disorders.

The general survey of the county, on the other hand, gave an estimated rate of 16.4 per 1000, obtained by combining actual cases found and an estimate of abnormal cases in the schools.

Hutterite Communities

In the Hutterite population of North and South Dakota, Montana, and Alberta, 8542 persons were screened for mental disorder. A list of possible cases was prepared for each colony, 29 per cent originating from private physicians, 21 per cent from mental hospitals, and the remainder from various other secondary sources. Of the 2000 persons interviewed by the study staff, 298 were examined by the psychiatrist. Nineteen colonies were studied intensively, to such an extent that no case of mental disorder was believed undiscovered. Information about the remaining 74 colonies came from informants, with occasional staff visits to 65 of the colonies. The established prevalence of psychoses did not appear to be directly related to intensity of field work, although a definite statistical correlation was demonstrated between that variable and the frequency of neuroses and personality disorders.

The authors presented rates of lifetime morbidity (active and inactive cases). However, we have calculated rates based entirely on active cases by obtaining a composite of the three categories of screening intensity. Our rates are 16.7 per 1000 for all disorders, 4.7 (fifteen years and over) for psychoses, and 11.5 (fifteen years and over) for neuroses.

Tennessee

After gathering secondary source data, the investigators surveyed intensively the entire population of three rural districts, constituting 15 per cent of the population of the county, plus a random sampling of urban residents. The case rate for the three districts (all present or past mental illness) was 123.7 per 1000, for the rest of the county 64.5, and for the entire county 69.4. Of 1721 cases in the latter group, 156 were or had been psychotic, compared with 99 current or former psychoneurotics. The small number of neurotics was attributed to deficiencies in reporting by physicians and in institutional records. Staff members interviewed or examined 55.5 per cent of the 1721 cases; the remainder were determined from information drawn from secondary sources.

Prevalence of cases active on the census day are calculated as 46.7 per 1000 for all disorders, 4.9 for psychoses, and 3.6 for neuroses. Rates for the intensive survey are not presented because they included but did not separate active and inactive cases.

The Baltimore and New Jersey surveys of the Commission on Chronic Illness were multiphasic.

Baltimore

The Bureau of the Census sampled 3828 households (one of every 80 in the city) and completed interviews of 97.7 per cent. Interviews consisted of health questions asked of the informant about himself and others in the household. About 10 per cent of the approximately 12,000 individuals were selected as a sample for clinical evaluation. Persons were put in one of three categories ranging from maximum disability to no disease or short-term disability. Individuals were selected for clinical evaluation by subsampling the three groups in proportions ranging from 100 per cent of those reporting the maximum disability to 6 per cent of those with no disease. In order to obtain estimates for the population as a whole, evaluation findings were weighted in inverse proportion to the sampling rate for the group. Patients in institutions were excluded from household interviews and consequently from clinical evaluation. The diagnosis of psychiatric conditions was by internists, with or without psychiatric consultation. Rates of prevalence were 108.6 per 1000 for all mental disorders, 4.3 (sixteen years or older) for psychoses, and 52.6 for neuroses.

New Jersey

Cases identified by household interview of 4246 families (13,113 individuals or 91 per cent of all families in a probability sample of one third of Hunterdon County) were divided into six groups related to assessment of chronic conditions; these groups in turn were sampled differentially for complete evaluation. About seven out of eight conditions classed on the basis of household interviews as mental, psychoneurotic, or personality disorder were confirmed by clinical examination.

Prevalence rates were 138 per 1000 for all disorders and 2 per 1000 for psychoses.

Eastern Health District

Both surveys of the Eastern Health District relied on secondary sources of information. The 1933 study obtained 3796 histories for consideration from psychiatric and sociological points of view. In 1936, 43 sources yielded 3337 active cases that were psychiatrically diagnosed and classified in terms of the social problems they presented.

Prevalence rates in 1933 were 44.5 per 1000 for all disorders, 8.18 (fifteen years or older) for psychoses, and 2 for neuroses. The 1936 rates were 60.5 for all disorders, 6.6 (ten years or older) for psychoses, and 10.7 for neuroses.

DIAGNOSTIC CRITERIA

The standards adopted for recognizing a person as having a mental disorder are a highly important variable in prevalence or incidence rates derived from epidemiologic surveys. The extent to which the observed rate represents the actual variation depends more on this element than on any other factor. The eleven surveys employed a variety of diagnostic criteria and methods. Even where similar cases were included in each count, the internal categories and diagnostic techniques often differed materially. Moreover, the same scheme of classification used in two different studies did not refer necessarily to the same kinds of illness, although the names of the divisions were the same.

Thomas Szasz (1957, p. 406) sought to justify this in the following comment:

It is apparent at once that the social situations in which so-called psychiatric observations are made are diverse, and yet it is generally assumed that one and the same system of classification should be useful for all of them . . . we cannot expect to be able to take a system of psychiatric nosology developed in one situation and expect it to be meaningful and serviceable in another.

Nassau County

The study was concerned with the relationship between social maladjustment and mental disorder. Individuals were classified by two independent systems, medical and sociological. Most of them were judged socially maladjusted, because maladjustment (as indicated by county agency records) was the basis for seeking mental disorders in the major portion of the study. Decision was based on interview information, case histories from agencies canvassed, and modified intelligence tests for individuals suspected of being mentally retarded. The opinion of trained psychiatrists determined the final diagnosis. The major medical classifications were:

1. *Constitutional disorders*
   Recoverable psychoses
   Recurrent psychoses
   Chronic psychoses without deterioration
   Chronic psychoses with deterioration
   Epilepsy
   Arrests of development
   Huntington's Chorea

2. *Disorders of exogenous origin*
   Traumatic psychoses
   Alcoholic psychoses
   Syphilitic psychoses

3. *Other groups*
   Senile psychoses
   Arteriosclerotic psychoses (non-syphilitic)
   Brain tumor
   Cretinism and myxedema

4. *Disorders of uncertain nature or etiology*
   (Neuroses were not mentioned)

Major sociological classifications were:

Retardation in school	Inebriety
Truancy, unruliness, etc.	Drug habits
Sex immorality	Domestic maladjustment
Vagrancy	Medical cases
Criminal tendency	Other groups
Dependency	No maladjustment

A separate classification applied to school children:

Feeble-minded	Epileptic
Psychopathic personality	Probably feeble-minded
Psychotic	Retarded

Eastern Health District (1933)

Cases were limited to socially visible mental disorder as reported by secondary sources. The diverse terminology and classification used by some of the original sources led to formulation of a two-part classification system as follows (condensed form):

A. *Reaction type*
   Psychotic
   Post-psychotic
   Psychoneurotic
   Epileptic
   Psychopathic
   Maladjusted, not included in the above types

B. *Psychiatric and social problems presented by the individual in 1933*
   Adult personality deviations

Behavior problems in children
Home care cases
Suicide
Alcoholism
Drug addiction
Marital difficulties
Family difficulties
Work adjustment difficulties
Difficulties in relations with social agency
Sex difficulties
Problems of delinquency
School maladjustment

Eastern Health District (*1936*)

Information was copied directly from secondary source case files. Psychiatric diagnoses were accepted at face value, the latest one in a given case being taken. An attempt was made to keep data comparable with the 1933 study. As in the earlier survey, a twofold classification system (psychiatric and sociological) was employed, although the classification schemes of the two surveys were not identical.

The psychiatric classification in abbreviated form and based in part on the *Statistical Manual for the Use of Hospitals for Mental Disease* (American Psychiatric Association, 1934) was as follows:

Psychosis
Psychoneurosis
Psychopathic personality
Personality disorder (adults)
Behavior disorder (children)

Minor or possible disorder
Epilepsy
Mental deficiency
School-progress problem
Adult delinquency

Included under social problems were:

School maladjustment	Sex problems
Delinquent behavior	Alcoholism
Work-adjustment difficulties	Drug addiction
Marital difficulties	Suicide
Difficulties over relation with social agency	Institutionalization

Tennessee

Roth and Luton used 87 diagnostic categories to classify three broad forms of mental illness:

A. *Mental disorders, personality and behavior problems*
B. *Mental deficiency*
C. *Organic and miscellaneous cases*

A lifetime diagnosis was derived for each individual according to the subcode of diagnostic terms. Diagnoses were arranged in categories ranked by severity. Each individual could be given as many as six diagnoses. The most severe problem during the life of the individual was considered the primary diagnosis.

A "social diagnosis" had the aim of describing adequacy of adjustment. Lifetime diagnoses included both psychiatric and specific descriptive categories. On the basis of the social diagnosis, cases were considered as active or inactive on the census day and further rated for degree of adjustment. Curiously, 183 of 203 persons assigned a primary social diagnosis of "mental deficiency" were noted as having no problems.

The 87 primary psychiatric diagnoses included such conditions as "nervous irritability" under *Psychopathic Traits,* "shy type" under *Special Personality Types,* and "home environmental factors," "multiple birth," and "normal individual" under *Organic and Miscellaneous*. Conceivably, such categorization was an attempt to identify persons with potential mental health difficulties. With such a spread of characteristics considered abnormal or potentially abnormal, a place would seem to exist in the case count for about every resident in the county.

Hutterite Communities

All persons with a history of mental illness from birth to August 31, 1951, and alive as of December 31, 1951, the date of a population census, were counted as cases. The diagnostic categories employed were: psychosis, psychoneurosis, mental defect, epilepsy, and personality disorder. Cases were classified as active, improved, or recovered according to the condition of the individual in the summer of 1951. All diagnoses made were reviewed twice, once in the fall of 1951 and again in July 1952. A first diagnosis was based on a classification used by James Coleman (1950); the final diagnosis was based on the *Diagnostic and Statistical Manual* of the American Psychiatric Association (1952). Cases were rediagnosed to conform to the American Psychiatric Association categories for two reasons: (1) additional information had been obtained about the cases by 1952, warranting review of the original designations; and (2) they believed the American Psychiatric Association divisions would become standard for future studies and wanted their categories to be comparable.

The clinically more severe disease was listed as the primary diagnosis where there was a choice of several. The validity of including epileptics among persons with mental disorder was questioned; the individuals listed as epileptic were without psychosis or mental retardation. They were included to permit comparison with earlier studies.

Interdisciplinary verification was not regarded as an adequate substitute for independent test of reliability of diagnosis by a disinterested expert not involved in the original field work. However, time and funds were not available for an independent check.

Illness was judged according to five presumed etiological indices:

1. *Genetic,* including evidence of familial transmission, although in some cases the latter may be indicative of cultural continuity rather than genetic linkage.

2. *Organic,* including infectious, traumatic, glandular, and neurological variables.

3. *Intrapersonal,* covering basic needs and subjective and emotional factors.

4. *Interpersonal,* including the effect of all social relations.

5. *Cultural,* including the role of values, religion, and ideology.

One hundred Thematic Apperception Tests, twelve Rorschach, and 125 specially constructed sentence completion tests were given. Questions dealing with the five indices of etiology were memorized by the interviewers. Written tests measured the emotional adjustment of children. One of these tests was a modification of the SRA Youth Inventory; the others are not identified. Public-school teachers were questioned, and an adaptation of the Rating Scale for Pupil Adjustment, developed by the Michigan Department of Public Health, provided ratings by Hutterite religious teachers. Evaluations of school children by the investigators and by the teachers did not always correspond. Discrepancies were attributed partly to less intensive screening than for adults and partly to differences in standards for norms and expectations between teachers and staff.

Baltimore

Individuals were classified according to major diagnostic and impairment categories of the *Diagnostic and Statistical Manual* (American Psychiatric Association, 1952). Although a psychiatrist did the actual classifying, internists selected the cases for his review. Numbers, therefore, were a function of the visibility of symptoms to a general diagnostician.

Salt Lake City

Respondent judgment was accepted in enumerating cases of mental illness in sampled families. Apart from the interviewer's observations and comments, no other criteria were brought to bear in judging the number of persons mentally ill. Overt symptomatology or admission of illness determined the psychiatric category. All debatable information was discounted, and no diagnosis was made if data were uncertain or if the individual was under sixteen. A rather singular classification system was used:

Schizophrenia (irrefutable delusions, etc.) and involutional states of psychotic proportions.

Hysterical symptoms: paralyses; polysurgical patients; stuttering, etc.

Definitely anxious persons unable to cope with problems; phobias; decompensating compulsions.

Alcoholism.

Suicide gestures: other "acting out" symptoms of severe proportions.

Senile psychoses or other organic psychoses.

Psychosomatic illnesses: ulcerative colitis, asthma, ulcer, etc.

The interviewers accepted at face value the comments of respondents about themselves and their families despite the demonstrated tendency of most persons to rationalize deviant behavior in others.

Syracuse

Persons in the Bellin and Hardt study were graded according to an eight-point scale ranging from zero (psychotic) to seven (very well). Ratings of zero to three were interpreted as an indication that individuals might be eligible for legal commitment to mental hospitals. Three investigators rated each person independently, and two out of three ratings in the zero to three categories established the person as in "poor mental health," the state with which the case count was concerned.

Both this study and the Downing and Gruenberg study avoided specific classifications. The latter appears to have dealt with more severe disease; namely, persons judged incapable of caring for themselves because of severe mental disability.

New Jersey

The findings of the Commission on Chronic Illness were based on the ultimate judgment of the physician member of the evaluation team. The pediatrician was said to have a psychiatric orientation because he had worked with a psychiatrist for several years. The internists had had little, if any, psychiatric work in their training as specialists. In general, the judgment of the individual with psychiatric training would be considered the more valid, and the difference in visibility of symptoms would tend to make the total rate (children and adults) invalid if the data were founded on very different evaluations. Although each case was diagnosed according to the psychiatric classifications of the American Medical Association and the World Health Organization, two categories of mental disorder were used for statistical reporting purposes: psychosis, and psychoneurosis and other personality disorders. This classification is understandable because the researchers were interested in *all* chronic disease, not mental illness only.

Midtown

The system of classification of mental disorders was based on operational definitions geared to questionnaire items. Two psychiatrists independently classified each respondent according to degree of mental health. A standard diagnostic classification system was not used for several reasons: The questionnaire items had been tested on a mixed patient group; they were general, not specific indicators; the psychiatrists did not see the respondents and declined to make a diagnosis on secondhand information; and, finally, no diagnostic system was found acceptable.

Symptoms were weighed for number, severity, and significance, and health was rated in one of six categories according to the estimated degree of subsurface mental disturbance or overt disability shown by the subject in daily life.

Those with no overt disability, the "unimpaired," were distributed within three categories:

1. *Well:* free of significant symptoms.

2. *Mild disturbance:* some intrapsychic disturbance, but functions well.

3. *Moderate disturbance:* varying intrapsychic symptoms, but functions pretty well.

Those with intrapsychic symptoms sufficiently severe to impair overt functioning, the "impaired," also were divided into three categories:

4. *Marked disturbance:* pronounced intrapsychic symptoms with some difficulties in life spheres.

5. *Severe disturbance:* pronounced intrapsychic symptoms with constriction in role functioning.

6. *Incapacitated:* near total or total disability in major life roles.

POPULATIONS

The final variable influencing survey findings is really a galaxy of intangibles, the characteristics of the population. The intrusion of procedural variables makes it difficult to evaluate the extent of this influence on the results of a given study.

A Variety of Variables

Mental illness has been investigated in relation to age, sex, social class, economic status, occupation, residence, marital status, religion, ethnic background, and many other factors.

Although a demonstrated association of certain variables with
mental illness does not prove causal relationship, it often has
distinct value in suggesting lines of future research.

This problem may be illustrated by an example, recalling
that incidence is the number of new cases occurring within a
specified time period, and prevalence is a measure of how
many persons are ill at a particular time.

In determining either rate for a particular age group, the
number of cases is related to the total number of persons in
the group. Combining weighted values for each age group
gives an age-adjusted index of the proportion of mentally ill
in the total population studied. But the observation of only a
few cases over sixty-five years of age would scarcely warrant
the conclusion that there is little mental illness in this older
age group. Perhaps few in the population reach an age of
sixty-five; the observed number of cases might then be a
majority of all persons over sixty-five, giving a high rate. On
the other hand, if a great number of the population attain that
age, the cases would be a small proportion and the rate would
be low.

Age-specific rates still give no indication of the relationship
of mental illness to sex in this group. In most populations, females outnumber males after age sixty-five, but a high rate of
mental illness for the age group would not necessarily indicate
a high rate for females. The sex distributions for the group and
among the mentally ill would determine that fact. For the
population at large, age-adjusted rates for males and females
are required.

Someone now might suggest that rates may be influenced
by the number of millionaires in the population, which neces-
sitates computation of age-sex-adjusted rates for each eco-

nomic group. And so with the effect of religion, nationality, social status, migration and immigration, marital status, allergy, and early bowel training. Plainly, it becomes impossible to hold all factors constant save the one being studied. Another adjustment for each new constellation of factors ends in a situation where the groups of people examined are so small that the fractionated results approach statistical absurdity.

All discernible variables cannot be taken into account; factors must be selected as relevant to the hypothesis to be tested. Selection, weighting, and correlation of variables are thus of prime importance.

An independent variable is a factor not influenced or determined by a dependent variable, in this case mental illness (to the degree that it is defined in the study). As Srole has ably set forth in Chapter 2 of the Midtown survey, age, sex, and ethnic background are independent variables, but marital status is not necessarily an independent variable. (It, as well as current socio-economic status and present religion, are reciprocal variables.) Different marital states may have different effects on persons of the same level of mental health; they also may be determined initially by the mental health of the individual. Educational attainment and income may be affected by mental illness, but limited educational and vocational achievement also may contribute to mental illness. More needs to be known about the intervening factors that account for the association of mental illness with a number of variables.

The Sample

Selection of a representative population sample is essential to sound statistical prediction. An adequate sample permits observations from which conclusions may be drawn about the general population. Because data are derived from only a part of the whole, such conclusions are subject to what is known as sampling error. However, sampling may be planned so that the probability of error remains within prescribed limits. The term *probability sampling* is properly applied only when every member of the population has a known probability of being chosen for the sample, and that probability is not zero. A standard error in the measure being estimated from the sample (the standard error of estimate) then can be applied to the results.

If an inventory of the population does not exist, *area sampling* may be used. A map is divided into small areas, and a sample of these is taken.

In *simple random sampling,* the probability of selection is equal for all members of the population.

Stratified sampling divides the population into more or less homogeneous groups. Random samples are taken from each stratum, and an estimate for the entire population is made by weighting the average of the estimates from the different strata.

Cluster sampling takes aggregates of the units in which interest centers. A random sample of households has less sampling error than a sample of blocks; and a sample of individuals, less than one of households.

Chunk sampling is through common access rather than by probability. It applies, for example, to individuals on the records of an agency or group of agencies. Similarity of the chunk to the population for which generalization is sought lends no real validity to the generalization, for the chunk may differ in just one respect, the characteristic to be measured!

Nassau County

One purpose of this study was to examine the hereditary nature of social maladjustments. No single sampling technique was used; the family was the unit of study because all near relatives of individuals suspected of being abnormal were also considered. Four districts in the county were examined intensively. Because case-finding was wholly through public records in the general survey of the county, probability sampling was never attempted.

The objective was to find those persons known to public authorities as socially maladjusted who also were mentally ill. This aim naturally influenced statistical procedure. Abnormals were compared with normals having no known abnormal near relatives, with normals who did have such relatives, and with persons of doubtful normality. The four groups were compared for age and sex distribution, nativity, race, education, weekly income, and marital status. The abnormal cases found in the community were compared with 1910 census figures for the United States in respect to parentage, nativity, and race. They were arranged by psychiatric identity and by nature of social maladjustment.

The number of cases per 100,000 population was presented only according to psychiatric classification in order to illustrate prevalence of the several varieties of mental disorder. This measure neglected age and sex distribution of the general population; the current census data did not permit the author to refine his calculations. The suggestion was advanced that an intensive (nonsampling) study was best for populations under 25,000, with the comment that the nonintensive part of the study suffered from lack of normals for comparison.

The sophistication of this study was unusual. The recommendation for comparable surveys of other populations and a resurvey of the same area with different personnel and objectives was well ahead of its time.

Eastern Health District (1933)

This one-year prevalence survey used a chunk sampling technique, because data were collected from secondary sources. The Baltimore district under study was approximately one square mile containing a bad slum area and lower middle-class neighborhoods. Rates for total mental disorder were given for the district and separately for white and Negro residents. No adjusted total rate was derived. Crude prevalence rates for psychosis were based on population over fifteen years of age and were computed for males and females, with whites and Negroes treated separately. Personality disorders were analyzed by race, sex, and geographic subdivision. The two wards of the area and four subdivisions of each were the basis for analysis of findings among white residents. The data were further refined in respect to Jews and non-Jews, and by type of household, where size of household, economic status, and "household condition" served as indices. Age-adjusted rates were used whenever groups were sufficiently large for statistical accuracy; a standard error was supplied with each rate. Because of chunk sampling, extension of the conclusions drawn from this study to other and larger populations is without profit.

Eastern Health District (1936)

This later study covered the same area and likewise used chunk sampling, together with information from the National Health Survey. This was also a one-year prevalence study.

Seventy-seven per cent of the persons in the District were white, compared with 81 per cent for the city as a whole. The study group constituted roughly one fifth of the population of Baltimore. No significant difference in sex distribution of Negroes and whites existed. There was an excess proportion of Negroes below age fifteen and between twenty-five and forty-five years.

Age-adjusted rates for psychosis were given for Negroes and whites because of the difference in age composition. One-day prevalence rates, and incidence rates as indicated by first admission to an institution, were computed for psychosis; the two racial groups were compared. Age-adjusted rates for neurosis were given by sex and race, and separately for children. White "adult neurotic" persons were analyzed by family income. Epileptics and the mentally retarded were classified by age, sex, and race. Separate rates were calculated for persons aged ten to fourteen years and twenty years and over, as these age periods were considered of particular importance. Total cases found (as identified in a household census of the National Health Survey) were related to the number reported in the National Health Survey with the suggestion that completeness of coverage might be investigated through this index for any grouping of the population. Again, no conclusions can be drawn from these data about other populations because of sampling technique.

Tennessee

Cases in Williamson County were those known to public authorities plus referrals by key informants and staff members living in the area. The procedure followed gave an estimate of the number of persons regarded by themselves or others as needing psychiatric help, but the sample was no more representative than those of the two Eastern Health District studies. An "unbiased" sample of the total population of the county was thought to have been obtained by adding to the population of three rural districts a strictly random sample of an urban population. This sample of about 15 per cent was suggested to be a representative cross section of the county, although evidence to support this statement was not presented.

The study was termed a one-day prevalence study. Only 55.5 per cent of cases ascertained were examined or interviewed by the staff. Lifetime diagnoses were used; we do not consider this scarcely recognized procedure to be legitimate in a one-day prevalence study that supposedly enumerates persons ill on the particular census day. Rates were not adjusted for age and sex. Those for Negroes and whites were compared. Age distributions of referred cases were given, but they included both active and inactive cases. Forty per cent of cases counted were judged as mentally deficient; only 10 per cent of the mentally retarded were diagnosed as having active problems. Statistical analysis and information about sampling technique was inadequate and incomplete.

Hutterite Communities

No sampling procedure was followed; the case count of mental disorder was in terms of (1) lifetime morbidity (total number ever ill), (2) active case morbidity (subdivided into those actively ill and those improved as of August 31, 1951), and (3) other cases (those recovered as of the above date and those with status unknown). Lifetime morbidity was determined for each diagnostic category, and the rate further refined in relation to three levels of screening intensity and then examined for statistical significance. The validity of the case count of living psychotics was tested by comparing estimated lifetime morbidity rates as of 1951 and 1930. The Hutterites were studied as a unique group; the results obtained do not apply to any other population.

Baltimore

The Bureau of the Census drew a probability sample of addresses from the 1950 census lists, together with representation from new housing. One of every 80 households was selected, by equal chance, to constitute the basic sample; it was then divided to give 52 subsamples. Members of each household were interviewed, excluding those in institutions.

Ten per cent of the basic survey group was then chosen as a subsample for purposes of clinical evaluation. Different sampling proportions were used for persons reporting various health conditions, ranging from 6 per cent of those reporting no illness to 100 per cent of those reporting serious illness. Mental illness was not one of the conditions differentially sampled.

Only 63 per cent of the sample selected for clinical evaluation participated, with the result that the data collected concerned a self-selected group within each differentially sampled subgroup. These findings were adjusted for differences in participation and further weighted by age, sex, and color to minimize bias arising from these differences. The persons evaluated were then distributed almost identically with the population of the city according to age, color, and sex.

Weighting of the data following demographic comparison of the age-sex-race composition of the clinical sample and comparison of clinical participants with nonparticipants does not necessarily assure accuracy of rates for mental illness. Participants may differ from nonparticipants in one characteristic, mental health. If a higher proportion of the mentally disturbed elect not to participate, the resulting rates will constitute an understatement.

New Jersey

A systematic probability sample on an area basis included one third of the families in a primarily rural county having a population of 42,736 by the 1950 census. All individuals in each family were divided into six strata related to assessment of chronic conditions from interview data. The institutionalized were placed in a separate stratum for sampling purposes. The six strata were differentially sampled for complete clinical evaluation. The response rate of the total stratified sample was 72 per cent, the number of respondents 846. Data on mental illness were derived from the clinical examination. The reported rates include the institutionalized, whereas the Baltimore study of the Commission on Chronic Illness excluded such persons.

The Hunterdon study data were weighted according to sampling ratios and made no assumptions about nonresponse.

Salt Lake City

The residents of eight separate blocks of the city constituted the sample. The areas chosen were considered fairly representative of the general population. The sample and the general population are stated to have been compared with respect to age, education, income, and occupation. However, information is provided neither on the procedures followed nor on sources of information. Twenty-five consecutive families in each sample block were chosen for interview. Of the 200 families, 175 cooperated. Total persons in the sample aged over sixteen (the only age group considered) was not given. Approximately one third (111) of this adult sample was judged mentally ill. The amount and kind of mental illness in various social strata of the sample were presented, but social level was not defined. The 17 cases of psychosis identified are hardly enough to warrant an attempt to relate this condition to social status.

Syracuse

The Bellin and Hardt investigation had to do with all non-institutionalized persons over sixty-five years of age in six census tracts. The tracts were recognized as not representative of Syracuse. They were selected because of high rates of first admission to mental hospitals for patients with psychoses of old age. Eighty-nine per cent (1541) of the specified population were successfully interviewed. Rates for mental disorders were computed by marital status and sex, and the findings weighted for physical health, socio-economic status, and age.

The Downing and Gruenberg study appears to have been concerned with the same population, although the basis for selection of the six tracts is not stated. Eighty-eight per cent (1534) of attempted interviews were completed. The criteria for mental illness were more exacting than those of the companion study, and the findings therefore not comparable.

Midtown

The first operational phase of this study was concerned with the existing records of all treatment facilities available to residents of the study area. This particular section of Manhattan has a high population density with a great range of socio-economic levels. The records were used without sampling to obtain a one-day treated prevalence rate and a one-year treated incidence rate.

The second phase of the study was an interview investigation of a random probability sample of that part of the population aged twenty to fifty-nine. The sampling ratio was approximately 17 per 1000, each individual in the sample being from a different residence. Eighty-seven per cent of the group selected were successfully interviewed, giving a sampling ratio of 15 per 1000 with a variance of 2.5 per cent. The respondents were checked against census data and found to approximate the demographic composition of the population universe. Persons in institutions were not included.

Individuals were distributed among six categories of mental health. Mental illness findings were analyzed in relation to age, sex, marital and socio-economic status, generation in the United States, religion, and national and rural-urban origin, in that order. Relevant preceding variables were held constant as each new variable was retested after general correlational data had been examined.

Statistical and methodological procedures were accurately described. Numbers of cases were provided with rates to facilitate cross-checking; all variables were operationally defined. This was the most complete study reviewed.

PREVALENCE FINDINGS

The prevalence rates for total mental illness as defined by each survey and, wherever possible, for psychoses and neuroses, are presented in Table 3. When prevalence rates were not given, values have been computed so far as the data permit. Each prevalence rate is for the shortest period covered in the particular survey. Disease-specific rates for psychosis and neurosis are included because they are the broad traditional diagnostic divisions in clinical psychiatry.

Table 3—Eleven Community Surveys of Mental Illness Prevalence Rates per 1000

Survey	Total Mental Disorders	Psychoses	Neuroses
Nassau County	36.4[a]		
Eastern Health District (1933)	44.5[b]	8.18[b] (over 15)	2.0[b]
Eastern Health District (1936)	60.5[b]	6.6[b] (over 10)	10.7[b]
Tennessee	46.7*[a]	4.9*[a]	3.6*[a]
Hutterite Communities	16.7*[c]	4.7*[c] (15 and over)	11.5*[c] (15 and over)
New Jersey	138.0[a]	2.0[a]	
Baltimore	108.6[a]	4.3[a] (over 16)	52.6[a]
Salt Lake City	circa 333.0[a] (over 16)		
Syracuse (Bellin and Hardt)	232.0[a] (65 and over)		
Syracuse (Downing and Gruenberg)	53.0[a] (65 and over)		
Midtown	233.0[a] ("impaired") (20 to 59)		

* Our calculation.
a one-day rate (day of examination or interview considered equivalent to a single day).
b one-year rate.
c three-month rate.

The range of rates is so great as to defy generalization. Obviously the recorded values are affected strongly by differences in study design, by study definitions, and by classification systems. These variables preclude projection of results to other similar populations or to a broader universe. Neither can the rates be interpreted as reflecting differences in the frequency of mental illness in the several communities. Such differences doubtless exist, but their extent cannot be determined from studies made thus far.

VIII

A New Look At Cause: The Controlled Field Study

THE BETTER conceived of the community surveys have been important markers along the way to an understanding of mental illness as it manifests itself in populations. In some instances they have provided information that enabled the community studied to take directed action not otherwise possible. Although the findings cannot be projected to other or larger populations, they are a significant source of leads to factors in causality, capable of subsequent test under controlled conditions and by multiple measurements.

Prevalence surveys reinforce evidence concerning the demographic characteristics of mental illness, such as race, age, and sex, derived from studies of patients in mental hospitals. The unique contributions of the prevalence surveys are their observations about the way people live and the manner and extent to which a way of life is reflected in the occurrence of mental disorder.

The principle that disease is the result of an interaction between an organism and its environment is illustrated by the origin and behavior of this group of morbid processes. Environment makes itself felt by way of area of residence, kind of housing, occupation, social class, economic status, marital state, community organization, and an imposing variety of similar influences.

Genetics may contribute to causality as it determines variations in anatomic structure and physiologic function, extending its influence ultimately, perhaps, to social maladjustment. Ethnic status, growth and development, and the reaction to stresses of an increasingly complex environment are other considerations. These are the kinds of lines of causality that emerge most prominently from the population surveys.

The various studies analyzed in Chapter VII have prepared the ground for a more sophisticated methodology. The field-testing of a wide range of survey techniques has yielded a growing body of knowledge about their applicability to the study of mental illness in population groups. The variation among results in itself has directed attention to the crucial importance of sampling techniques, population, correlation of variables, and other links in the procedural chain.

The most striking lesson from the prevalence survey is the stern and endlessly repeated admonition that true progress toward a grasp of mental illness in the population, as in the individual, will not begin until the validation and universal acceptance of a precise diagnostic system. Clinical diagnosis of mental disease is difficult at best for the well-trained psychiatrist; the areas of ambiguity that beset the clinician are even more diffuse under field conditions, away from the diagnostic advantages of the clinic and hospital examination. Less precise though they necessarily must be, the methods of the field still have to be exact enough to apply with some measure of meaning to material numbers of people. The skin test for susceptibility to diphtheria, for instance, lacks the precision of antitoxin titration, but it is reliable enough for practical measurements of population resistance.

Knowledge of the total dimensions of mental illness in the United States—even in specific population groups—is of some value perhaps, but it is difficult to see how this information can be applied effectively to prevention and control unless action rests on a comprehension of etiology. Public health administrators need to know enough about the complex of causative factors to gauge the regularity with which each disease entity occurs in terms of time, place, and people. The search for causality may well contribute more to the design of a universal diagnostic system—and to the emergence of a practical epidemiologic method in this field—than any combination of efforts to deal with the gross problem from the starting point to current knowledge.

THE CONCEPTUAL FRAMEWORK

Studies of patients in institutions were of great importance in establishing qualitative standards for the classification and diagnosis of mental illness. The next logical step was to employ these standards in the community, to seek clues concerning the incidence of mental illness in the population, treated and untreated. The community survey produced many interesting and significant leads. Essentially, however, it is a "fishing expedition," incapable by design or objective of putting to test the hypotheses it suggests.

Continued epidemiologic progress in the field depends on the construction of orderly, well-controlled field experiments designed to identify and quantitate, one by one, the various factors that have been advanced as being involved in causality. A knowledge of causality is fundamental to the prevention and control of mental disease. It must be related to specific disease entities. Leads, as we have seen, are drawn from clinical knowledge of mental illness, laboratory investigation, studies of hospitalized patients, and prevalence surveys of various population groups.

What are the effects of population density, for example, on the prevalence of mental disorders? Are there certain common genetic traits that condition the resistance or susceptibility of homogeneous ethnic groups? Can the temporal development of schizophrenia and some of the behavioral illnesses be correlated with endocrine and other developmental changes? What is the effect of an aging population on the age distribution of mental disorders? What associations may there be between mental disease and other mental and physical illnesses (separate entities, rather than psychosomatic)? Is a physically healthy population less susceptible to mental disease? Does mental illness appear in seasonal peaks? Is nutrition related to mental health? How does the role of the individual within the social framework affect his ability to withstand stress? What is the role of the value system in mental illness?

THE EXPERIMENTAL DESIGN

The first task is to select a lead for investigation and evaluation, a choice that rests on the strength of the supporting evidence from which to formulate a hypothesis, on judgment as to its probable significance within the total causative complex, on the inclinations and capabilities of the investigator, and finally—and not least important—on the availability of practical techniques for measurement of the factor under the conditions of the field. Out of this process emerges a working concept of causality. Then, within this framework, the field is surveyed; all available pertinent data bearing on the concept are gathered in preparation for the design of an actual controlled experiment.

There are two kinds of controlled field experiments for testing a hypothesis of causality. One, the proband method, begins with index cases of the recognized disease entity and works backward in a search for cause, examining features of the patient's environment and constitution. The other begins with the population, seeks out by case-finding those affected and again proceeds, some times retrospectively, in the search for cause. Short-term studies of both types are usually more productive in defining the size and nature of the problem than in identifying specific causes. Long-term incidence investigations stand a better chance of discovering cause by their employment of repeated examinations and analysis of changes over a period of time. Both of these field techniques are aimed at fixed population samples, although the proband method is not necessarily representative.

AREAS OF INVESTIGATION

Suicide

Epidemiologic analysis of suicide illustrates the proband approach to mass mental illness. Suicide is the only end result of mental disorder that can be accurately measured by death;

deaths provide the index case from which a retrospective search for cause proceeds. The reliability of data concerning suicide is comparable to that for tuberculosis, and statistics are relatively inclusive. Whereas the social stigma associated with suicide lead to some false reporting, the opposite error of including nonsuicidal death is probably rare. Within these limits it is possible to relate suicide to the general population as a component of deaths from all causes.

The phenomenon is the end result of a causative complex and obviously should not be confused with factors that are directly responsible for precipitating the final event. Erich Lindemann, in a panel discussion (John E. Gordon *et al.*, 1950), postulated a gradient of suicide for the purpose of establishing a specific relationship between a common under-lying pattern of conflict and its end point. His concept de-mands a definition of psychiatric conditions that are far less exact than suicide itself. For this reason, an analysis of success-ful attempts at suicide must deal with a small segment of the total morbid state—the true population problem—but it has the advantage of providing the investigator with a clear-cut index of overt mental illness in a sharply bounded area. Under-standing of the total process requires an expression of mor-bidity, or numbers of cases, of all grades of severity. This is a requisite for the comprehension of any disease that may produce death, such as poliomyelitis; with suicide, as with polio, morbidity is a factor of the various gradations constitut-ing the total process.

Suicide can, therefore, be viewed in classical epidemiologic fashion as satisfactorily as most of the communicable diseases, considerably better than most other noninfectious mass dis-eases, and far more precisely than any other mass mental disorder, including those whose origin is associated with a specific agent (Gordon *et al.,* 1950).

Good records of suicide in France date back to 1817 and, with some limitations, are available for Germany over much the same period. Data from England, Wales, and the United States cover a shorter interval.

Because the incidence of suicide in the United States is only about 1.8 per 1000 per year, a population survey is impractical, although field studies encompassing large cities might prove feasible.

Alcoholism

A long-term incidence survey would be useful in tracking down the causes of varying degrees of alcoholism in the population and the determinants of its progression from a mild habit to an addictive disease. Most studies have concentrated on the exaggerated and atypical aspects of drinking, and the results have not been particularly profitable. A knowledge of the natural history of alcoholism is needed as the point of departure toward the prevention and control of the underlying mental pathology of which it is the overt expression.

The usual definitions of alcoholism preclude the finding of all but the extreme cases. Without a classification gradient, a count cannot be made, and without a count the assembling of significant epidemiologic data is scarcely possible.

If alcoholism is arbitrarily defined as the internal use of alcohol—regardless of periodicity, place, portion, or practice— the population can be divided into those who do and those who do not partake of it (Gordon, 1958b).

Drinkers, however, deserve to be further divided according to the amount they drink and its effect on them. We are look-

ing for categories of effect in terms of death, defect, and disability—the three criteria by which mass health problems are
assessed. It is reasonable to assume that limits can be determined within which there are no measurable ill effects from
alcohol; in fact, it may occasionally be beneficial.

The biologic gradient of disease, a concept that has enhanced the understanding of other mass diseases, may be
applied to alcoholism. One fraction of the total population
abstains from the use of alcohol. A second takes it in limited
amounts with little material variation from day to day. A
third shows the symptoms of alcoholism. The fourth is characterized by addictive and advanced alcoholism accompanied
by organic and mental changes—the end point in the gradient.

By analogy with diphtheria, an infection, the abstainers are
the susceptibles in the population, those who do not have the
disease. Others may be immune by reason of moral or other
conviction. The customary or social drinker corresponds to
the person with inapparent diphtheria infection lacking clinically discernible disease, but nevertheless infected. The symptomatic drinker matches the individual with atypical modified
diphtheria. Clinical alcoholism is analogous to classical diphtheria, and its exaggerated organic or psychic deterioration
corresponds to malignant or hemorrhagic diphtheria.

The concept has practical value. Scarlet fever, diphtheria,
and many other infections were never fully understood until
the total process was seen to include inapparent infection as
well as clinical disease. The latent or subclinical infection is of
material advantage to a population because its immunizing
effect leads to protection against the clinical disease.

Each component of the disease gradient is usually measurable in respect to the death, defect, and disability it causes.

The extent of alcoholism, and its effects on the health of a population, can thus be compared as a function of time. The significance of these comparisons depends on evaluation of the end result, clinical alcoholism, against the total gradient, the use of alcohol. Just as the importance of tuberculosis in a population cannot be judged solely by the amount of pulmonary cavitation present, the dimensions of the problem of alcoholism can be exaggerated or minimized by reason of the relative proportions of its parts as they are evident and appreciated, or hidden and unevaluated. Rabies exists in man as a clinical disease, for all practical purposes. Poliomyelitis, on the other hand, is largely submerged below the level of clinical recognition. These relations are undefined for alcoholism. Because a majority of adults in the United States use alcohol, abstinence is not the norm. Which part of the gradient corresponds to infection and which to disease? Even more important, which component of alcoholic "infection" is truly latent, having no discernible ill effects on the host, and which is "incubatory infection," with the probability of erupting into actual, clinical disease? In other words, which users of alcohol will eventually become alocholics, and why?

The gradient of a pathologic process is altered from time to time by the action of environmental factors; measurements of these changes have been restricted for practical purposes to the clinical manifestations of the disease, in this instance the end stages of alcoholism. A base line is needed by which to judge changes either in the total number of drinkers in a population or in their distribution along the gradient. An increase or decrease in the total amount of alcoholism may be a general phenomenon affecting all classes of drinkers, with the endemic level rising or falling equally and vertically; or it may result from a specific environmental influence on a specific group of drinkers of such magnitude as to be reflected in the total.

The most striking deviation from established behavior is that which corresponds to the common source epidemic of infectious disease. Such sharply developing outbreaks occur in alcoholism and often have significant effects on general rates of death from that condition. During World War II, such a point outbreak occurred among displaced persons in southern Germany. It originated in a single source of liquor contaminated with methyl alcohol, and 86 persons died within forty-eight hours.

Most mass processes of health and disease are subject to cyclic changes in frequency, and alcoholism is no exception. Prohibition and other changes in the social environment, such as industrialization, unemployment, and war, have resulted in alterations of the pattern. In the European Theater during World War II, more deaths were reported among American soldiers from alcohol poisoning than from all communicable diseases combined. Alcoholism and spring burgeon together in many countries, and in almost all parts of the world long-term trends are seen, upward or downward movements in the frequency of alcoholism over the years. Alcoholism is generally endemic, regardless of locale, and its prevalence is commonly modified in the long run by cyclic changes in frequency and in the short run by variations corresponding to true epidemics.

Inadequacies in the reporting of deaths from alcoholism and variations in diagnosis are obstacles to the determination of its incidence in the total population. Almost no data suggestive of occurrence are available. Such knowledge as exists is derived from a variety of such indirect measurements as arrest for drunkenness or first admission to institutions.

It is high time for alcoholism to be studied by the modern field methods of epidemiology. Prevalence studies of this condition are sometimes incorporated in general health surveys, and an evaluation of prevalence or incidence may be included to advantage in nutritional studies. The latter combination with alcoholism would be decidedly practical because some of the stigma attached to personal discussion of the condition might be removed during case-finding interviews by taking an indirect approach via questions concerning diet.

There are good reasons for selecting the family as the unit for observation in field studies of alcoholism; the effects extend beyond the drinker to all members of his immediate family.

Postpartum Psychoses

Psychosis after childbirth is an example of a mental disorder whose onset or, perhaps more accurately, whose overt manifestation is precipitated by a specific event, in this case maternity. It has the advantage of being readily identifiable clinically and of occurring under conditions that are adaptable to control (Clayton L. Thomas and J. E. Gordon, 1959).

As in the case of alcoholism, the patient suffering from a postpartum psychosis can be observed retrospectively and prospectively. Unlike alcoholism, however, this disorder appears too infrequently to fall within the scope of a population study. Consequently it is investigated to advantage by the proband method, following and comparing equal numbers of cases and normal controls of similar backgrounds drawn from a large maternity hospital.

Psychosomatic Disorders

Psychosomatic diseases such as peptic ulcer, allergic reactions, multiple sclerosis, and ulcerative colitis are physical illnesses appearing as manifestations, to varying degrees, of underlying mental or emotional disturbance. Hence, the physical symptoms reveal the index case.

At present, frequency of occurrence of most psychosomatic illnesses—especially allergic reactions and peptic ulcer—can only be conjectured. It is suggested that each entity be investigated initially by the proband technique. Should the incidence prove sufficiently great, further studies could be undertaken on a population basis.

IX

Conclusion

MENTAL ILLNESS in the United States is a public problem of alarming proportions, alarming not only because there is something seriously wrong with the mental health of millions of Americans but because so little solid progress has been made toward understanding or even defining this problem. Many years of painstaking and difficult investigation and study will be required before the first effective steps can be taken in the direction of mass prevention and control.

No health problem could be of greater or more appropriate concern to the epidemiologist; certainly it would seem to rank among his greatest current challenges; it may be the area in which he will make his most important contribution to the welfare of mankind.

At present, however, the application of epidemiologic methods to the study of mental illness is in a most rudimentary and tentative form. Epidemiology was able to assume a major role in the conquest of communicable disease only after sufficient scientific knowledge had been accumulated to provide grist for its interpretive mill. A comparable degree of knowledge concerning mental illness does not now exist.

Emphasis has been placed recurrently in this volume on the imperative need to disentangle the threads of causality from the fabric of the disease. An effective beginning can be made by applying the established principles of controlled field experimentation to the study of discrete disease entities characterized by a minimum of elusive symptomatology. In this fashion a working method for the epidemiologic analysis of a wider range of more complex mental disorders may gradually emerge.

The communicability of mental illness, as discussed in Chapter V, has not been completely established. Nevertheless, this concept offers an area of research that could be explored profitably from the standpoint of possible factors in the origin of mental illnesses.

The community survey has had an important part in the evolution of a more sophisticated epidemiology of mental illness. Yet this form of population prevalence study as it has developed in recent years has largely outlived its usefulness, primarily because of the absence of real control over the multitude of variables that tend to distort data necessarily gleaned from a relatively brief period of observation. A long-term carefully designed field study of an established entity, such as coronary heart disease in the Framingham, Massachusetts, Heart Survey, would be a logical successor to the present prevalence survey.

An epidemiological approach to mass mental disease necessarily must be the same, in its working principles, as any public health approach to a physical disease. Thus, we should like to emphasize the desirability of efforts to establish close cooperation between the various public health and other helping agencies.

We must again emphasize the importance to all segments of the field of a universally accepted diagnostic classification of mental illness. The nosology agreed upon by the American Medical Association and the American Psychiatric Association need not be taken as doctrine; but the inevitable shifts and refinements in diagnosis of the future should be incorporated within these classifications in an orderly and extremely conservative fashion.

Mental illness must be understood in the individual before it can be dealt with in groups of individuals and populations on the public health level. Epidemiologic and statistical leads can of course bring to light facets of etiology that have managed to elude observation of the individual. But in the final analysis, epidemiology offers no easy detours around basic scientific research, the foundation for the prevention and control of all disease.

References

American Psychiatric Association, 1934. *Statistical manual for the use of hospitals for mental disease.* State Hospitals Press.

——, 1952. *Diagnostic and statistical manual.* American Psychiatric Association Mental Hospital Service.

Bellevue Hospital, 1903. *A nomenclature of diseases and conditions and rules for the recording and filing of histories for Bellevue and allied hospitals.* Martin B. Brown Printing and Binding Co.

Bellin, S. S., and Hardt, R. H., 1958. Marital status and mental disorders among the aged. *Amer. Sociol. Rev., 23* (2): 155.

Bell, L. V., 1844. *Twenty-sixth annual report of the McLean Asylum for the Insane, 1843.* James Loring Press.

Clark, R. E., 1949. Psychoses, income and occupational prestige. *Amer. J. Sociol., 54* (5): 443.

Cohen, B. M., and Fairbank, Ruth, 1938a. Statistical contributions from the Eastern Health District of Baltimore. I. General account of the 1933 mental hygiene survey of the Eastern Health District. *Amer. J. Psychiat. 94* (5): 1153.

—— and ——, 1938b. Statistical contributions from the mental hygiene study of the Eastern Health District of Baltimore. II. Psychosis in the Eastern Health District in 1933. *Amer. J. Psychiat., 94* (6): 1377.

——, ——, and Greene, Elizabeth, 1939[a]. Statistical contributions from the Eastern Health District of Baltimore. III. Personality disorder in the Eastern Health District in 1933. *Human Biology, 11* (1) : 112.

——, Tietze, C., and Greene, Elizabeth, 1939[b]. Statistical contributions from the mental hygiene study of the Eastern Health District of Baltimore. IV. Further studies on personality disorder in the Eastern Health District in 1933. *Human Biology, 11* (4) : 485.

Cole, Nyla J., Branch, C. H. H., and Shaw, Orla M., 1957. Mental illness. *A.M.A. Arch. Neurol. & Psychiat.,* 77 (4) : 393.

Coleman, J., 1950. *Abnormal Psychology and Modern Life.* Scott.

Commission on Chronic Illness, 1957. *Chronic Illness in the United States.* Vol. IV. *Chronic Illness in a Large City.* Harvard University Press.

Dayton, N., 1940. *New Facts on Mental Disorders.* Charles C Thomas.

Downing, J. J., and Gruenberg, E. M., 1957. *Some differentials in the prevalence of mental symptoms in an aging population.* Mental Health Research Unit, N.Y. State Dept. Mental Hygiene. (mimeographed.)

Dunglison, R. J., 1860. Statistics of insanity in the United States. *N. Amer. Medico-Chirurgical Rev.,* 4 (4) : 656.

Eaton, J. W., and Weil, R. J., 1955. *Culture and Mental Disorders.* Free Press.

Elkind, H. B., 1927. The epidemiology of mental disease. *Amer. J. Psychiat.,* 6 (4) : 623.

——, 1938. Is there an epidemiology of mental disease? *Amer. J. Public Health, 28* (3) : 245.

Emerson, H., 1932. The magnitude of nervous and mental diseases as a public health problem. In F. E. Williams (Ed.), *Proceedings of the 1st International Congress on Mental Hygiene,* Vol. 1. International Committee for Mental Hygiene, Inc.

——, 1939. Epidemiology a possible resource in preventing mental disease. In F. R. Moulton (Ed.), *Mental Health,* American Association for the Advancement of Science.

Faris, R., and Dunham, H. W., 1939. *Mental Disorders in Urban Areas: An Ecological Study of Schizophrenia and Other Psychoses.* University of Chicago Press.

Felix, R. H., and Bowers, R. V., 1948. Mental hygiene and socio-environmental factors. *Milbank Memorial Fund Quart.,* 26 (2) : 127.

Freeman, A. W., and Cohen, B., 1939. Preliminary observations on epidemiology of mental disease. *Amer. J. Public Health,* 29 (6) : 633.

Goldhamer, H., and Marshall, A., 1953. *Psychosis and Civilization.* Free Press.

Golin, M., 1959. How deadly the thought. Exploring communicability of ideas and attitudes. *J.A.M.A., 171* (2) : 182.

Gordon, J. E., 1955. Population pathology. *Tr. & Stud. Coll. Physicians Philadelphia, 23* (1) : 1.

———, 1958^a. Medical ecology and the public health. *Am. J. M. Sc., 235* (3) : 337.

———, 1958^b. Epidemiology of alcoholism. *New York J. Med., 58* (11) : 1911.

———, Lindemann, E., Ipsen, J., and Vaughan, W., 1950. An epidemiologic analysis of suicide. In *Epidemiology of Mental Disorder.* Milbank Memorial Fund.

———, O'Rourke, E., Richardson, F. L. W. Jr., and Lindemann, E., 1952. The biological and social sciences in an epidemiology of mental disorder. *Am. J. M. Sc., 223* (3) : 316.

Hollingshead, A. B., and Redlich, F. C., 1958. *Social Class and Mental Illness: A Community Study.* Wiley.

Hunt, W. A., and Wittson, C. L., 1949. Some sources of error in the neuropsychiatric statistics of World War II. *J. Clinical Psychol., 5* (4) : 353, 355.

Jordon, E. P. (Ed.), 1942. *Standard nomenclature of disease and standard nomenclature of operations.* American Medical Association.

Landis, C., and Page, J., 1938. *Modern Society and Mental Disease.* Farrar and Rinehart.

Lemkau, P., Tietze, C., and Cooper, Marcia, 1941. Mental-hygiene problems in an urban district. *Mental Hygiene, 25* (4) : 624.

———, ———, and ———, 1942[a]. Mental-hygiene problems in an urban district. II. *Mental Hygiene, 26* (1) : 100.

———, ———, and ———, 1943. Mental-hygiene problems in an urban district. III. *Mental Hygiene, 26* (2) : 275.

———, ———, and ———, 1943. Mental-hygiene problems in an urban district. IV. *Mental Hygiene, 27* (2) : 279.

Logie, H. B. (Ed.), 1935. *Standard classified nomenclature of disease.* The Commonwealth Fund.

Malzberg, B., 1940. *Social and Biological Aspects of Mental Disease.* State Hospitals Press.

National Committee for Mental Hygiene, 1918. *Statistical manual for the use of institutions for the insane.* National Committee for Mental Hygiene.

Odegard, O., 1932. Emigration and insanity. *Acta Psychiatrica et Neurologica, Supplementum IV.*

Plunkett, R. J. (Ed.), 1952. *Standard nomenclature of diseases and operations.* American Medical Association.

Pollock, H. M., 1941. *Mental Disease and Social Welfare.* State Hospitals Press.

Ray, I., 1871. Proceedings of the Association of Medical Superintendents. *Amer. J. Insanity, 28* (2) : 310.

Rennie, T. A. C., Srole, L., Langner, T., and Opler, M., In Press. *Midtown Manhattan: The Mental Health Story.* McGraw-Hill.

Rosanoff, A. J., 1917. Survey of mental disorders in Nassau County, New York, July–October, 1916. *Psychiatric Bull., 2* (2) : 109.

Roth, W. F., and Luton, F. H., 1943. The mental health program in Tennessee. *Amer. J. Psychiat., 99* (9) : 662.

Rowntree, L. G., McGill, K. H., and Hellman, L. P., 1945. Mental and personality disorders in selective service registrants. *J.A.M.A., 128* (15): 1084.

Szasz, T. S., 1957. The problem of psychiatric nosology. *Amer. J. Psychiat., 114* (5) : 406.

Thomas, C. L., and Gordon, J. E., 1959. Psychosis after childbirth. *Am. J. M. Sc., 238* (3) : 363.

Trussell, R. E., and Elinson, J., 1959. *Chronic Illness in the United*

States. Vol. III: *Chronic Illness in a Rural Area.* Harvard University Press.

World Health Organization, 1948. *Manual of the international statistical classification of diseases, injuries and causes of death.* World Health Organization.

Yarrow, Marian R., Schwartz, Charlotte, Murphy, Harriet, and Deasy, Leila, 1955. The psychological meaning of mental illness in the family. *J. Soc. Issues, 11* (4): 12.

Appendix

Joint Commission on Mental Illness and Health

PARTICIPATING ORGANIZATIONS

American Academy of Neurology

American Academy of Pediatrics

American Association for the Advancement of Science

American Association on Mental Deficiency

American Association of Psychiatric Clinics for Children

American College of Chest Physicians

American Hospital Association

American Legion

American Medical Association

American Nurses Association and The National League for Nursing (Coordinating Council of)

American Occupational Therapy Association

American Orthopsychiatric Association

American Personnel and Guidance Association

American Psychiatric Association

American Psychoanalytic Association

American Psychological Association

American Public Health Association

American Public Welfare Association

Association for Physical and Mental Rehabilitation

Association of American Medical Colleges

Association of State and Territorial Health Officers

Catholic Hospital Association

Central Inspection Board, American Psychiatric Association

Children's Bureau, Dept. of Health, Education and Welfare

Council of State Governments

Department of Defense, U.S.A.

National Association for Mental Health

National Association of Social Workers

National Committee Against Mental Illness

National Education Association

National Institute of Mental Health

National Medical Association

National Rehabilitation Association

Office of Vocational Rehabilitation, Department of Health, Education and Welfare

United States Department of Justice

Veterans Administration

MEMBERS

Kenneth E. Appel, M.D.
Philadelphia, Pa.

Walter H. Baer, M.D.
Peoria, Illinois

Leo H. Bartemeier, M.D.
Baltimore, Maryland

Walter E. Barton, M.D.
Boston, Massachusetts

Otto L. Bettag, M.D.
Springfield, Illinois

Mr. George Bingaman
Purcell, Oklahoma

Kathleen Black, R.N.
New York, New York

Francis J. Braceland, M.D.
Hartford, Connecticut

Hugh T. Carmichael, M.D.
Chicago, Illinois

J. Frank Casey, M.D.
Washington, D.C.

James M. Cunningham, M.D.
Dayton, Ohio

John E. Davis, Sc.D.
Rehoboth Beach, Delaware

Neil A. Dayton, M.D.
Mansfield Depot, Conn.

Miss Loula Dunn
Chicago, Illinois

Howard D. Fabing, M.D.
Cincinnati, Ohio

Rev. Patrick J. Frawley, Ph.D.
New York, New York

Mr. Mike Gorman
Washington, D.C.

Robert T. Hewitt, M.D.
Bethesda, Maryland

Herman E. Hilleboe, M.D.
Albany, New York

Nicholas Hobbs, Ph.D.
Nashville, Tennessee

Bartholomew W. Hogan, Rear Adm. M.C., U.S.N., Washington, D.C.

Louis Jacobs, M.D.
Washington, D.C.

M. Ralph Kaufman, M.D.
New York, New York

William S. Langford, M.D.
New York, New York

Miss Madeleine Lay
New York, New York

Jack Masur, M.D.
Bethesda, Maryland

Berwyn F. Mattison, M.D.
New York, New York

Ernst Mayr, Ph.D.
Cambridge, Mass.

Robert T. Morse, M.D.
Washington, D.C.

Ralph H. Ojemann, Ph.D.
Iowa City, Iowa

Winfred Overholser, M.D.
Washington, D.C.

Howard W. Potter, M.D.
New York, New York

Mathew Ross, M.D.
Washington, D.C.

Mr. Charles Schlaifer
New York, New York

Lauren H. Smith, M.D.
Philadelphia, Pa.

M. Brewster Smith, Ph.D.
Berkeley, Calif.

Mr. Sidney Spector
Chicago, Illinois

Mesrop A. Tarumianz, M.D.
Farnhurst, Delaware

David V. Tiedeman, Ed.D.
Cambridge, Mass.

Harvey J. Tompkins, M.D.
New York, New York

Beatrice D. Wade, O.T.R.
Chicago, Illinois

Mr. E. B. Whitten
Washington, D.C.

Helen Witmer, Ph.D.
Washington, D.C.

Luther E. Woodward, Ph.D.
New York, New York

OFFICERS

President: Kenneth E. Appel, M.D.
Philadelphia, Pa.

Chairman, Board of Trustees: Leo H. Bartemeier, M.D.
Baltimore, Md.

Vice-President: M. Brewster Smith, Ph.D.
Berkeley, Calif.

Secretary-Treasurer: Mr. Charles Schlaifer
New York, N.Y.

Vice-Chairman, Board of Trustees: Nicholas Hobbs, Ph.D.
Nashville, Tenn.

STAFF

Director: Jack R. Ewalt, M.D.
   Boston, Mass.
Consultant for Scientific Studies: Fillmore H. Sanford, Ph.D.
   Austin, Texas
Consultant in Social Sciences: Gordon W. Blackwell, Ph.D.
   Chapel Hill, North Carolina
Consultant in Epidemiology: John E. Gordon, M.D.
   Boston, Mass.
Associate Director for Administration: Richard J. Plunkett, M.D.
   Chicago, Illinois
Director of Information: Greer Williams
   Boston, Mass.
Associate Director and Consultant on Law: Charles S. Brewton, LL.B.
   Alexandria, Virginia
Librarian: Mary R. Strovink
   Boston, Mass.

Index

accidents, endemic nature of, 8
acting out, 34, 76
adaptation process, 31
admissions, community attitudes and, 42; diagnosis and, 25–27; symptomatology and, 52
adolescence, 31
age-adjusted index, 79
age distribution, in general population, 82; of referred cases, 85
age-sex ratios, 86
age-specific rates, 79
alcoholic psychoses, 69; diagnoses of, 25–27
alcoholism, 71, 76; controlled field studies in, 98–102; deaths from, 101; definition of, 98; epidemiological studies of, 102
American Medical Association, 22, 24, 77, 106
American Medico-Psychological Association, 21

American Neurological Association, 22
American Psychiatric Association, 21–24, 71, 73, 75, 106
Anopheles mosquito, 31–32
anthropologist, staff, 59
antibodies, 29
anxiety, 20, 75
area sampling, 81
Armed Forces, mental-illness nomenclature in, 23; psychiatric problems of, 9, 22, 39, 45
arteriosclerotic psychoses, 69

bacterial infections, mental disorders and, 29
Baltimore (Md.) Commission on Chronic Illness, 49–50, 57, 64, 76–77, 87; mental-illness studies in, 9, 43
Baltimore (Md.) community surveys, 50–51; case-finding techniques in, 66–67; diag-

[117]